Practice Companion

VOLUME 1

The McGraw·Hill Companies

www.WrightGroup.com

Printed in the United States of America.

Send all inquiries to:
Wright Group/McGraw-Hill
P.O. Box 812960
Chicago, IL 60681

ISBN 978-0-07-656528-3
MHID 0-07-656528-9

6 7 8 9 RMN 16 15 14 13 12

Contents

Unit 1

Week 1

Focus Question

What makes a good friend?

Week 2

Focus Question

What do friends share together?

Week 3

Focus Question

How is my family a part of who I am?

Unit 2

Week 1

Focus Question

How do plants and animals grow and change?

Week 2

Focus Question

How do things move and change?

Week 3

Focus Question

How does nature affect the way we move and change?

Unit 3

Week 1

Focus Question

What kinds of communities are there?

Week 2

Focus Question

What jobs are a part of my community?

Week 3

Focus Question

How do neighbors in a community play together?

Unit 4

Week 1

Focus Question

What are Earth's natural treasures?

Week 2

Focus Question

How do we use Earth's natural treasures?

Week 3

Focus Question

Why must we protect Earth?

My Weekly Planner

Week of ______

Theme Vocabulary ______

Differentiated Vocabulary ______

Comprehension Strategy and Skill

Strategy: ______

Skill: ______

Vocabulary Strategy ______

Spelling Skill ______

Fluency

Selection: ______

Writing and Language Arts

Writing form: ______

Grammar

Grammar skill: ______

Poem

Read the poem.

A Friend Can

by Harper Hess

When I need help,
who can help me?
A friend can help me.

When I want to play,
who can play with me?
A friend can play with me.

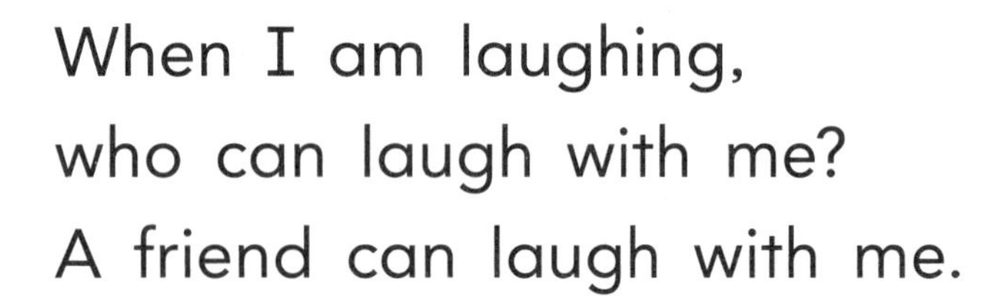

When I am laughing,
who can laugh with me?
A friend can laugh with me.

When I am sad, who can cheer me up?
A friend can cheer me up.

How well did you read? Circle your answer.

Directions: Follow the Teacher's Lesson Guide directions each day of the week. At the end of the week, students circle the face showing how well they read.

Sentences

problems	different	connected

Fill in the blanks.

1.  

Kids do ____________ things.

2. 

Kids help with ____________.

3. 

Mom, Dad, and I are ____________.

Directions: Read the sentences aloud with children. Have them choose the best vocabulary word from the box to complete each sentence.

Opposites

Circle the correct word.

1.

same **different**

2.

problem **solution**

3.

same **different**

4.

connected **apart**

Directions: Tell students: *Opposites are words that mean very different things, such as* up *and* down. Read the questions and have students circle the best word. 1. *Are these things the same or different?* 2. *Is this a problem or a solution?* 3. *Are these things the same or different?* 4. *Are these things connected or apart?*

High-Frequency Words

a	on	an	was
is	the	in	

Write.

1.

This is ___a___ tree.

2.

This is ______ apple.

3.

We are ______ school.

4.

______ cat is white.

5.

The book is ______ the table.

6.

I ______ sad, but now I am happy.

Directions: Review the high-frequency words with students. Then have them write the high-frequency word that best completes each sentence.

Find Important Information

Find big ideas.

Read. Check the most important idea.

Friends can like different things.

Sam wants to play catch. He likes baseball.

Pat wants to ride bikes.

She likes to be outside.

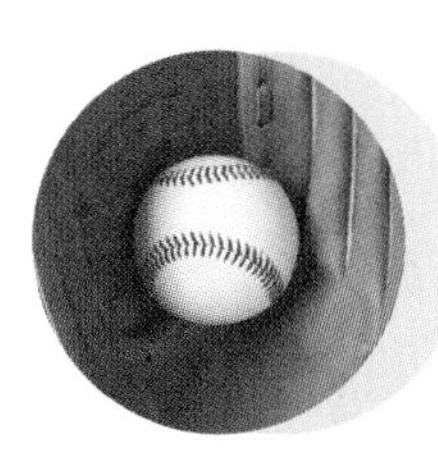

✓ ________ Friends can like different things.

________ Sam wants to play ball.

________ Pat wants to ride.

Read. Check the most important idea.

1. Jen is at the park.

"May I play?" asks Jen.

"Yes," says Pat.

Jen makes a new friend.

________ Jen is at the park.

________ "May I play?" asks Jen.

________ Jen makes a new friend.

2. This is my family. My family likes to have meals together. We are eating burgers for dinner.

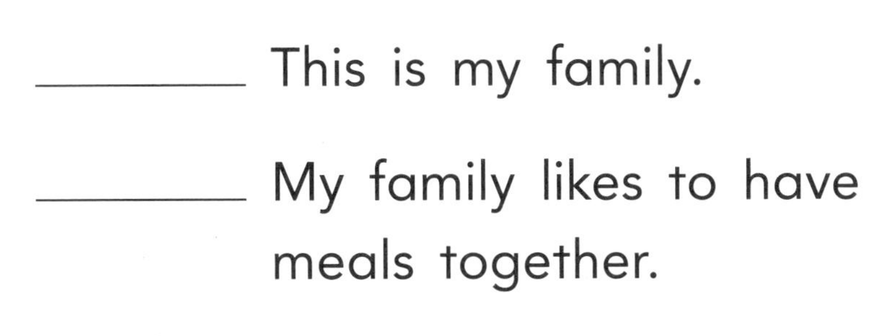

________ This is my family.

________ My family likes to have meals together.

________ We are eating burgers.

Directions: Read the story and the sentences on page 6. Explain that the check mark shows which idea is most important. Repeat for the stories on page 7. Students check the most important idea.

Use Context Clues

Some words in a sentence can help you understand new words.

He **chops** the apple into small bits.

Look at the words *apple* and *bits*.
They can help you understand *chops*.
It means "to cut small."

Circle the words.

This family likes to **hike**.

They walk in the woods.

Circle the words.

1. This family likes to **celebrate**.

   They are having a party.

2. Tod likes **sports**.

   He swims and plays soccer.

3. Jen is my **pal**.

   We walk to school together.

4. Dan feels **blue**.

   He even looks sad.

Directions: Read the text on page 8. Ask: *Which words help you understand* hike? Point out the words *walk* and *woods* as context clues. Help students understand that *hike* means "to take a long walk." Repeat for page 9.

Compare and Contrast

When you **compare** and **contrast**, you tell how things are alike and different.

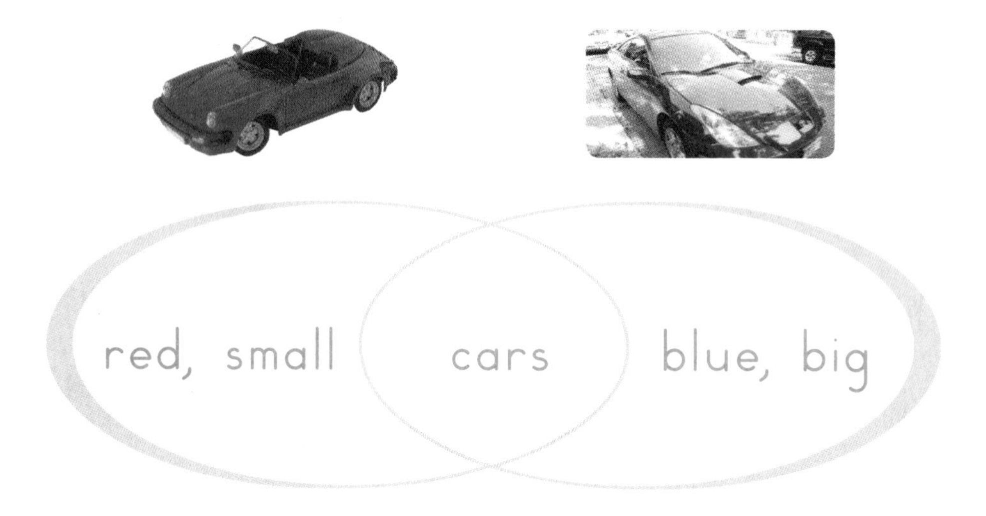

Compare the animals.

Directions: Show students how they can use a Venn diagram to compare and contrast. Then have students work in pairs to complete the bottom of the page.

Sentence Structure

Make a sentence.

1. happy I am

I am happy.

2. class are We in

3. blue is The house

4. dog is Your big

Directions: Students write the words in the correct order to build a sentence.

Question Words

Who are your friends?

What games do friends play?

When do friends play?

Where do your friends live?

Why are friends important?

Directions: Read each question to students, emphasizing the question word. Then have students discuss how the pictures relate to the question words. Students can refer to this page to help them generate Inquiry Questions.

My Weekly Planner

Week of

Theme Vocabulary

Differentiated Vocabulary

Comprehension Strategy and Skill

Strategy:

Skill:

Vocabulary Strategy

Spelling Skill

Fluency

Selection:

Writing and Language Arts

Writing form:

Grammar

Grammar skill:

Play

Read the play.

The Fort

by Sean Gomersil

Mother: Please turn off the TV for a while.

Liam: What should we do instead? Play video games?

Julian: Or play on the computer?

Mother: No. Why not build a fort? I will get you some sheets.

Liam: Can we use these chairs?

Julian: How about these pillows?

Mother: Sure! And here is some paper. You can make a sign to hang in front.

How well did you read? Circle your answer.

Directions: Students practice reading the selection aloud. Then they rate themselves using the faces on the bottom of the page.

Draw It

Draw.

Family Members

Directions: Students draw their family members. Encourage students to label the people with a name or a word that shows the relationship to the student, such as *Mom, Dad,* or *Papa.*

Related Words

You can be a **member** of a

team	family	class

Label the pictures.

1.

2.

3.

Directions: Discuss with students the different types of groups that have members: team, family, class. Then have students label each picture with a word from the box.

Short *a*

am	map	ham	sat	had
at	tap	hat	mat	all

Unscramble the words.

1. t m a mat
2. d h a ________
3. m a ________
4. p m a ________
5. h t a ________
6. a p t ________
7. t a ________
8. l a l ________
9. m h a ________
10. a t s ________

Directions: Students unscramble the words and write the correct spelling on the line.

Find Important Information

Find big ideas.

- Look for important information.

Read. Circle the most important idea.

Families can be different sizes.
Families can be small.
Some families have a few people.
Families can be big.
Some families have more people.

Read. Circle the most important idea.

1\.  

Friends like to play together.
They play ball. They jump rope.
Sometimes they play games inside.

2\. 

My sister helps me all the time.
She talks to me. She plays with me.
She helps me with my problems.

Directions: Remind students to look for the most important ideas when they read. Read the story on page 18. Explain that the circle shows which sentence has the most important idea. Repeat for the stories on page 19. Students circle the most important idea.

Use Picture Clues

Pictures can help you understand new words.

They play checkers.

Read. Circle the picture clues.

It is very **noisy**.

Read. Circle the picture clues.

1. It is so **peaceful**. The family is quiet.

2. His milk **spills** on the tray.

3. The toy car goes around the **loop**.

Directions: Read the sentence on page 20, emphasizing *noisy*. Ask: *Which parts of the picture help you understand* noisy? Point out the circled parts of the picture. Help students understand that *noisy* means "loud" or "not quiet." Repeat for page 21.

Compare and Contrast

Comparing things tells how they are alike.

Contrasting things tells how they are different.

Banana	Both	Orange
yellow	fruit	orange
long	you peel them	round

Camping is like home.
My family is together.
We tell stories in both places.

But it is different, too. When we go camping, we cook over a fire. We sleep in a tent.

Camping	Both	Home
outside		

Directions: Talk about the pictures and read the text. Students compare and contrast camping and home. Have students work in pairs to complete the chart.

Statements

A **statement** is a sentence that tells something.

A **period** is at the end of the sentence. It looks like this. **.**

This is a hat.

Add the .

My family likes bikes. I have a yellow bike
My mom has a blue bike My dad has
an orange bike We all ride together

Directions: Tell students that this story is missing 5 periods. Have students follow along as you read, listening for the end of each sentence. They add 4 periods at the correct places.

Investigation Sheet

1. My Books

2. What I Learned

Directions: Read each numbered item to students. Students write the book titles that they used to collect information for the Inquiry Question. Then they draw and write what they learned from the books.

Taking Tests

Here is a question about *My Connections:*

How can friends be alike? (Page 12)

Ⓐ One is older.
Ⓑ One is taller.
Ⓒ They like different things.
Ⓓ They like the same things.

What is the question about?

- Are friends alike because one is older? No, being different ages does not mean they are alike.
- Is it because one is taller? No, that is not alike.
- Is it because they like different things? No.
- Can friends be alike when they like the same things? Yes. D is the correct answer.

Directions: Remind students to pay attention to the directions, especially key words that tell how to answer the question. Read the questions aloud and then direct students to the pages on which the answers can be found.

Taking Tests

1. What is the most important idea on pages 8–9?

Ⓐ Some friends like to play games.
Ⓑ Friends don't care what they do.
Ⓒ Friends like to do things together.
Ⓓ Other friends look for shapes in the clouds.

2. What do friends do when there are problems? (Page 14)

Ⓐ They help each other.
Ⓑ They take turns.
Ⓒ They talk on the phone.
Ⓓ They disagree.

3. How are families alike? (Page 20)

Ⓐ They are small.
Ⓑ They celebrate Kwanzaa.
Ⓒ They do big jobs.
Ⓓ They care for each other.

4. What is the most important information on pages 22–23?

Ⓐ The boy makes a list.
Ⓑ There are leaves to rake.
Ⓒ Families work together.
Ⓓ The job doesn't seem big.

My Weekly Planner

Week of	
Theme Vocabulary	
Differentiated Vocabulary	
Comprehension Strategy and Skill	Strategy: Skill:
Vocabulary Strategy	
Spelling Skill	
Fluency	Selection:
Writing and Language Arts	Writing form:
Grammar	Grammar skill:

Monologue

Read the story.

The Different Duck

by Cory Firth

Have you heard of me?
Some kids call me Ugly Duckling.
It is not a nice name.

My brothers and sisters are small.
I am big.

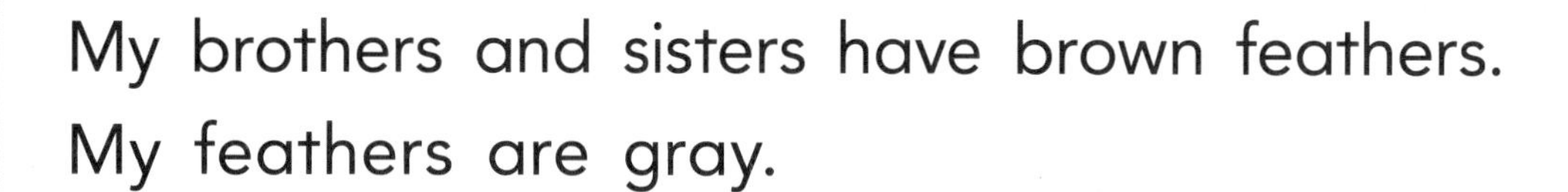

My brothers and sisters have brown feathers.
My feathers are gray.

My brothers and sisters are good at flying.
I am good at swimming.

My brothers and sisters are different from me,
but I like to be different!

How well did you read? Circle your answer.

Directions: Students practice reading the selection aloud. Then they rate themselves using the faces on the bottom of the page.

Draw It

grin to smile and show teeth

Draw.

Write.

Directions: Ask students what makes them grin. If necessary, suggest a birthday party or a water slide. Then students draw one thing that makes them grin. Write on the board: *This makes me grin.* Students write the sentence below their picture.

Picture Clues

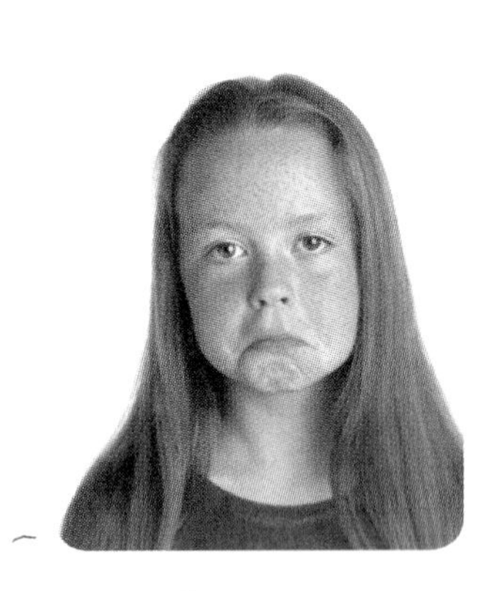

frown

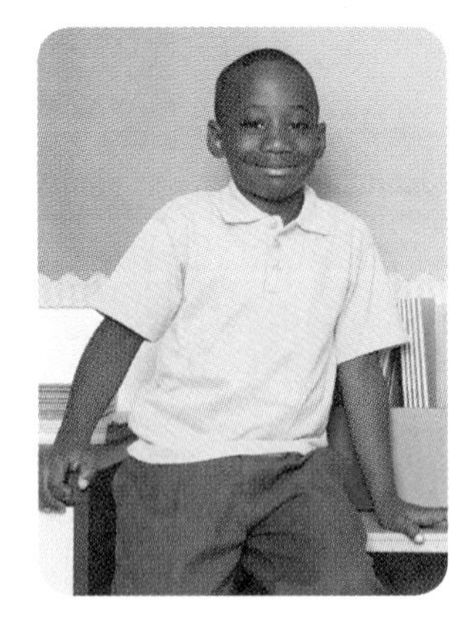

smile

grin

laugh

Fill in the blank.

1. When I am **very** happy, I grin from ear to ear.

2. When I am glad, I ________.

3. When I am sad, I ________.

4. When something is funny, I ________.

Directions: Discuss the emotions shown in the images above and review the names for each action. Then read the sentences aloud and have students identify and write the correct emotion for each blank.

Short *i*

it	him	hill	pin	little
sit	hip	pit	lip	didn't

Read the clue. Write the word.

1. hole in the ground pit
2. top of your leg ____________
3. sharp thing ____________
4. part of the mouth ____________
5. small mountain ____________
6. small ____________
7. did not ____________
8. that boy ____________

Directions: Review the short *i* words in the box. Then read each clue. Students choose the correct word from the box and write it on the line.

Make Inferences

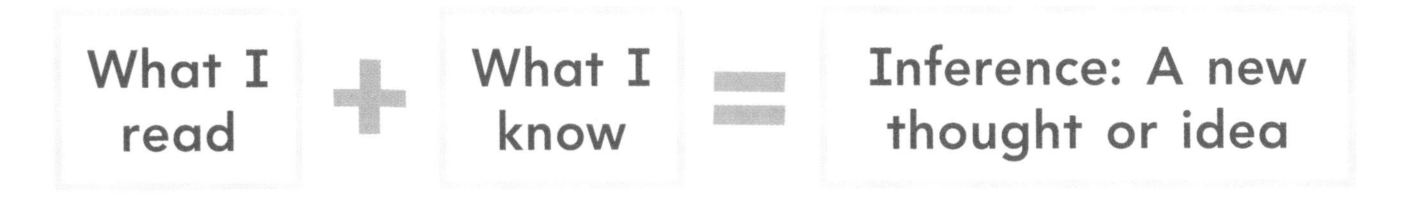

Use the Strategy

1. Think about what you read.

2. Look for clues in the story.

3. Think about what you already know.

4. Connect what you read to what you know.

5. Share your new thought or idea.

Read the story.

Tom and Lil are at the zoo.
Tom has one red balloon.
Lil has two yellow balloons.
Then Tom's string breaks.

"Oh, no!" says Tom.

Now Tom is sad.

"Here you are," said Lil.

"Thank you," said Tom.

Now Tom has one balloon again.

Circle.

1. It changes color.

It goes up into the sky.

2. He does not like the zoo.

He loses his balloon.

3. from Lil

from the store

Directions: Explain the steps on page 32. Then read the story on page 33. Ask each question and read the choices. Have students circle the correct inference. 1. *What happens to Tom's red balloon? It changes color or It goes up into the sky?* 2. *Why is Tom sad? He does not like the zoo or He loses his balloon?* 3. *Where does Tom get the yellow balloon? From Lil or from the store?*

Classify Words

Sorting words into groups can help you understand them.

Put the words in the chart.

dark	awake	moon	stars
light	sun	play	sleep

 Night	 Day
dark	light
moon	awake
stars	sun
sleep	play

Put the words in the chart.

boy	girl	brother	me
father	sister	mother	

F	M
girl	boy

Directions: Explain that the first column on p. 34 tells about the night and the second column tells about the day. Read the words in each column. Then remind students of the family members in *Hello, Baby!* Point out the two columns of the chart on p. 35 and explain that **F** stands for female, which means girl or woman, and **M** stands for male, which means boy or man. Read each word from the chart above. Students sort the words into the two groups.

Sound Devices

Sometimes writers use **rhymes** to make stories fun.

Sometimes they use **sound words** such as **thud** or **whee**.

rhyme Ⓐ **sound word** B

Write A next to lines that rhyme. Write B next to sound words.

1. Bob blows a bubble. The bubble goes pop!

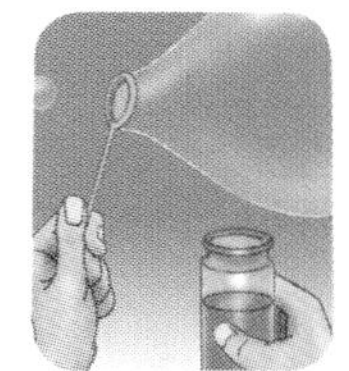

2. This is my cat. He has a hat. ________

3. Can this bird talk? No, the bird goes tweet.

4. I am not sad. I am not mad. ________

5. Dad has a flat tire. It goes hiss. ________

Directions: Make sure students understand *rhymes* and *sound words*. Read the sentences aloud and remind students to write A when they hear rhyme and B when they hear sound words.

Read and Respond

Answer the questions about the story *Hello, Baby!*

1. What did you like best about the story?

2. What did the sound words **wah** and **coo** make you think of?

3. What surprised you in the story?

Directions: Read each question. Students write their answers.

Identify Text Structure

Stories tell what happens first, next, and last.

Beginning	What happens first
Middle	What happens next
End	What happens last

Look at the pictures and listen. Write in order.

Beginning	Dot looks for her shoes
Middle	
End	

Directions: Read the story as students look at the pictures: *Dot cannot find her shoes. First, she looks in her bedroom, but they aren't there. Then she asks her mom, but her mom does not know. Finally, she finds her shoes outside.* Help students fill in the chart with the order of events in the story.

Questions

A **question** is a sentence that asks something.

A **question mark** is at the end of the sentence.
It looks like this. **?**

Circle the question.

1. Is the water cold?

The water is cold.

2. Can you play?

I can play.

3. I can push you.

Can you push me?

Directions: Read the sentences aloud. Have students circle the questions.

Book of Illustrations

What is a book of illustrations?

- It uses many pictures.
- It tells about an idea.
- It uses labels, letters, or words to tell more about pictures.
- It has a cover with a title and an author.
- The pictures can be photographs or drawings.

Directions: Read the information to students. Students study the example illustration from a book of illustrations. Discuss with them ways they might make a book of illustrations to tell about their Inquiry.

My Weekly Planner

Week of	
Theme Vocabulary	
Differentiated Vocabulary	
Comprehension Strategy and Skill	Strategy: Skill:
Vocabulary Strategy	
Spelling Skill	
Fluency	Selection:
Writing and Language Arts	Writing form:
Grammar	Grammar skill:

Lyric

Read the song.

Sisters

by Ricky Greenberg

We are sisters.
Oh yes, we are!
We know we like each other.
We like to play
And have lots of fun.
So does our brother.

I like red.
My sister likes blue.
It does not matter to brother.
Sisters and brother,
Oh yes, we are!
We like each other.

How well did you read? Circle your answer.

Directions: Students practice reading the selection aloud. The selection can be sung to the tune of "Pop Goes the Weasel." Then they rate themselves using the faces on the bottom of the page.

Write and Draw

different problems connected members grin

Word and Picture	What It Means

Directions: Review the words with students. Point out where they write a word, draw the picture, and write what the word means. Have them choose three words and fill in the chart.

Related Words

Draw lines.

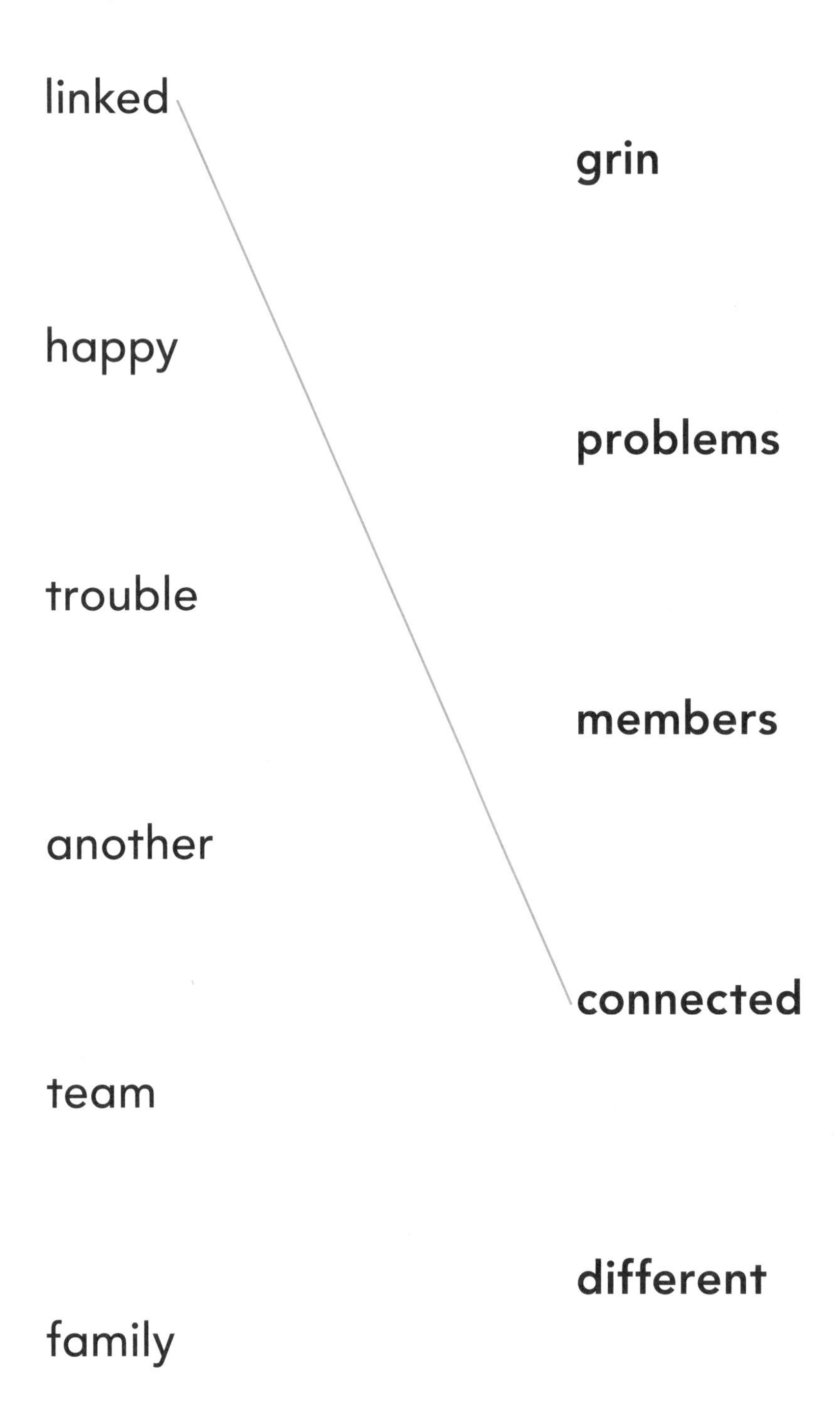

linked

grin

happy

problems

trouble

members

another

connected

team

different

family

Directions: Explain that related words are words that can go together. Read the words and have students draw a line from each related word on the left to a vocabulary word on the right.

Short *o*

not	lot	pop	cob	got
dot	hot	mop	cod	a lot

Unscramble the words.

1. t o l   lot

2. b c o

3. o t d

4. d c o

5. l a t o

6. t g o

7. p p o

8. o p m

Directions: Have students unscramble the words and write the correct spelling on the line.

Make Inferences

What I read	+	What I know	=	Inference: A new thought or idea

Read.

I want a friend. Who will play with me?

Make an inference.

What I read:	The boy is looking for a friend.
What I know:	I feel sad when no one plays with me.
Inference:	The boy feels sad.

Read.

It is the first day of school.
Matt does not know anyone.

A boy says, "I am Rob. Sit by me." They know they will be good friends.

Make inferences.

What I read:	
What I know:	
Inference:	

Directions: Read the text on page 46. Ask: *How does the boy feel?* Review how to use the graphic organizer to make an inference. Read the story on page 47. Ask: *How do you think Matt feels at the beginning of the story?* Have students fill in the boxes to make inferences. Ask: *How do you think Matt feels at the end of the story?*

Context Clues

When you don't know a word, look for **other words** around it to help you understand.

The fruit is **ripe** and ready to eat.

The words *fruit*, *ready*, and *eat* help you understand that *ripe* means "ready to eat."

Read.

"I can not go to the party," says Sal.

Mom says, "Do not be upset.

Do not worry.

You can go to other parties."

Word	Context Clues	Meaning
upset	worry	not happy

Find context clues.

1. There were many people in the **crowd**.
It was very loud.

Word	Context Clues	Meaning
crowd		

2. Mom loved the picture.
She put it in a wood **frame**.

Word	Context Clues	Meaning
frame		

3. Mr. Jones is our new **neighbor**.
He lives next door to us.

Word	Context Clues	Meaning
neighbor		

Directions: Read the text on page 48. Ask: *Which words help you understand* upset? Point out the context clues and the meaning on the chart. Repeat the process for each item on page 49. Help students find the context clues and understand the meanings of the bold words.

Identify Text Structure

Some stories tell what happens first, next, and last.

Beginning	1. What happens first
Middle	2. What happens next
End	3. What happens last

Read. Write 1, 2, or 3.

Ron wants to buy his brother a birthday present. Ron and his mom go to the store. Ron buys a toy car. It is bright red. The next day, Ron gives the present to his brother. His brother is very happy.

_______ Ron gives the present to his brother.

_______ Ron goes to the store with his mom.

_______ Ron buys a toy car.

Directions: Read the story aloud. Students write the numbers 1, 2, and 3 next to the events that happen in the beginning, middle, and end.

Exclamations

An **exclamation** is a sentence that shows a strong emotion.
An **exclamation point** is at the end of the sentence. It looks like this. **!**

Circle the exclamations. Add exclamation points.

1. This is fun !

   Is this fun ____

2. It is hot today ____

   How hot it is ____

3. May I go to the game ____

   I can go to the game ____

4. I love cats ____

   Do you like cats ____

Directions: Read each set of sentences aloud. Have students circle the exclamation and insert an exclamation point.

Investigation Sheet

1. My Books

2. What I Learned

Directions: Read each numbered item to students. Students write the book titles that they used to collect information for the Inquiry Question. Then they draw and write what they learned from the books.

Taking Tests

Here is a question about *Hello, Baby!*

How does brother feel about the baby?

How can you answer?

Tell what I read:

Brother wants to
show the baby.

Tell what I know:

Make an inference:

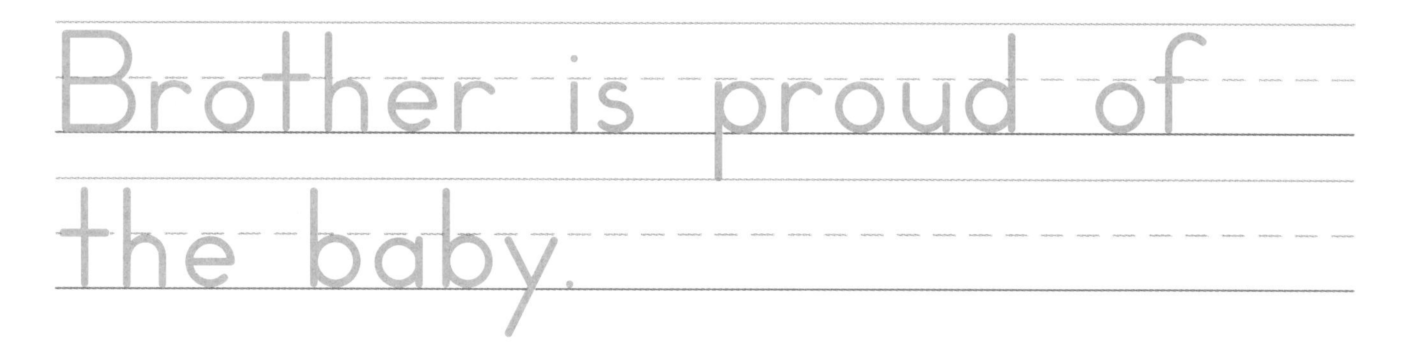

Directions: With the Literature Big Book open, work through both pages of Taking Tests with students. After reading "Tell what I read" on p. 53, ask students what they know about that. Then read "Make an inference." Remind them to pay attention to the directions, especially key words that tell how to answer the question.

Taking Tests

Here is another question about *Hello, Baby!*

How does the family feel when the baby cries?

Tell what I read:

Tell what I know:

Make an inference:

My Weekly Planner

Week of ______

Theme Vocabulary ______

Differentiated Vocabulary ______

Comprehension Strategy and Skill

Strategy: ______

Skill: ______

Vocabulary Strategy ______

Spelling Skill ______

Fluency

Selection: ______

Writing and Language Arts

Writing form: ______

Grammar

Grammar skill: ______

Poem

Read this poem aloud.

Apple Seed

by Edi Smith

A tree was full of apples.
A squirrel ate an apple
and left some seeds on the ground.

A dog buried a bone nearby
and covered the seeds in dirt.
Rain fell on the dirt.
The sun warmed the dirt.

Soon a tiny apple plant
peeked out of the dirt.
More rain fell.
The sun came out again.

The little apple plant grew some.
Then it grew some more!

How well did you read? Circle your answer.

Directions: Follow the Teacher's Lesson Guide directions each day of the week. At the end of the week, students circle the face showing how well they read.

Examples

Circle.

1. Which is **enormous?**

2. Which is used to **measure?**

 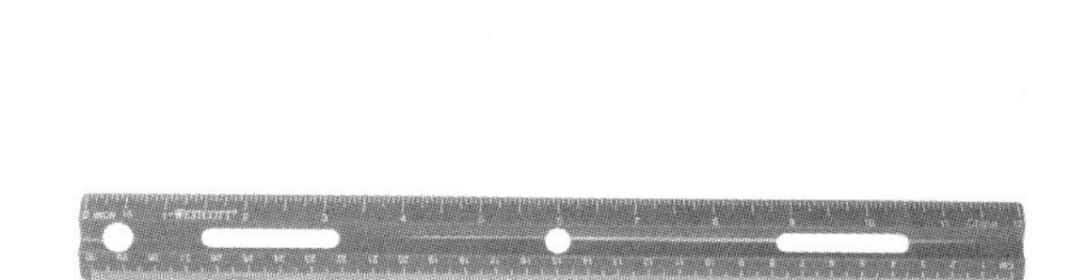 

3. Which is **enormous?**

4. The paper **measures** _____ pencils long.

2 3 4

Directions: Read the questions aloud with students. Discuss the answer choices and have students circle the best answer.

Use Pictures

Draw lines.

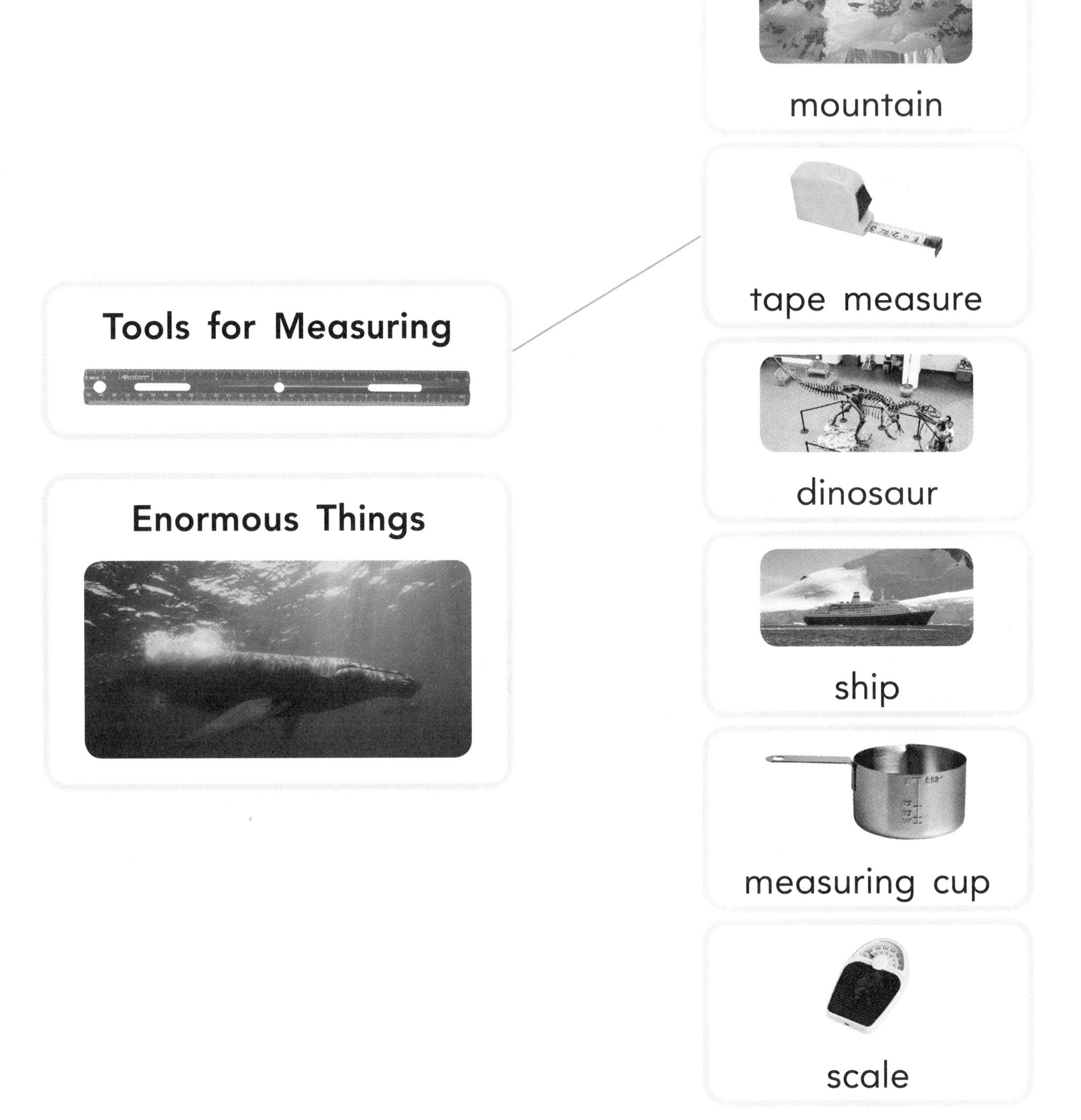

Directions: Read the labels in the right column. Students draw lines from the items in the left column to the pictures on the right.

l Blends

clap	clam	clip	plan	play
slam	slot	slid	split	the

Write the missing letters.

1. c 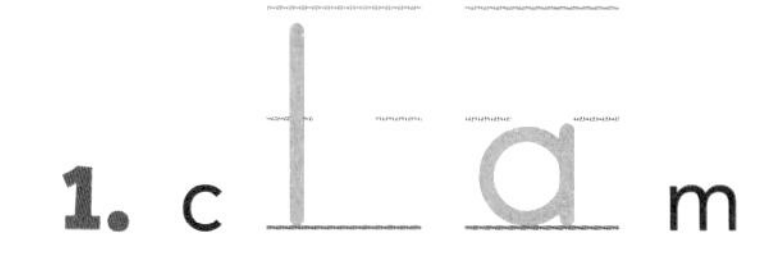 m
2. __ __ o t
3. __ __ __ i t
4. s __ i __
5. c __ a p
6. s __ a __
7. __ h __
8. __ __ a n
9. c __ i __
10. __ __ a y

Directions: Review the spelling words. Students fill in the missing letters for each word.

Make Predictions

Making predictions is making guesses about what will happen.

Using pictures can help you make predictions.

Read the title or the text.	+	Look at the pictures.	=	Make a prediction.

Look at the title and pictures. Fill in the chart.

Fighting Fires

Text	The title is *Fighting Fires*.
Pictures	There is a firefighter with a hose.
Prediction	It will be about how to fight fires.

Look at the title and pictures.
Fill in the chart.

The Flowers

Text	
Pictures	
Prediction	

Read.

It is mom's birthday.
Jenny wants to give mom
a present. She gets flowers.

Was your prediction correct? Circle. Yes No

Directions: Discuss with students the book cover on page 60. Read the answers in the chart. Then read the text and confirm that the prediction was correct. Repeat for page 61. If necessary, help students fill in the chart and check their predictions.

Use Context Clues

You can use **context clues** to figure out the meaning of a word you do not know.

There are different kinds of context clues.

- **Examples**
- **Words that mean the same**
- **Words that mean the opposite**

Read. Write the context clues and meaning.

The class hamster is missing.
He is lost. He is not in his cage. We will look until we find him.

Context Clues

Word
missing

Meaning
Missing means

Read. Write the context clues and the meaning.

The cat sits on my lap.
He is warm and <u>cozy</u>.
He is comfortable.

Context Clues

	warm	
Word cozy		**Meaning** **Cozy** means feeling warm and comfortable.

Directions: Read the text on page 62 and discuss the diagram for *missing*. Then read the text on page 63 to help students fill in the diagram for *cozy*.

Sequence Events

Sequence tells the order that things happen.

Beginning	What happens first
Middle	What happens next
End	What happens last

Look at the pictures and listen. Write in order.

_____ The baby bird grows bigger.

_____ The baby bird can fly.

_____ The mother bird feeds the baby bird.

Directions: Students look at the pictures as you read the story: *Every day, the mother bird flies to the nest and feeds the baby bird. The baby bird slowly grows bigger and bigger. Finally, the baby bird can fly.* Help students write the numbers in the boxes to show the beginning, middle, and end.

Nouns

Singular nouns tell about one thing.

Plural nouns tell about more than one thing. Add *s* or *es* to make a noun plural.

Circle the correct noun.

1.  The (dog / dogs) is white.

2.  The (frog / frogs) live in the pond.

3.  The (dish / dishes) are clean.

4.  The (book / books) is on the desk.

Directions: Review singular and plural nouns. Have students circle the correct noun for each sentence.

Collage

What is a collage?

- A collage has many different kinds of pictures.
- It tells about a topic or tells a story.
- A collage sometimes has labels to tell what the pictures mean.
- The pictures can be cut out of newspapers or magazines.
- The pictures can be photographs or drawings.

Directions: Read the headings and each bulleted phrase to students. Have students study the example of the collage. Students use this information to help them create a collage to share their Inquiry findings.

My Weekly Planner

Week of ______________________

Theme Vocabulary	
Differentiated Vocabulary	
Comprehension Strategy and Skill	Strategy: ______ Skill: ______
Vocabulary Strategy	
Spelling Skill	
Fluency	Selection:
Writing and Language Arts	Writing form:
Grammar	Grammar skill:

Newspaper Article

Read this article aloud.

Cats Win!

By Saskia Solotko

The Catskills Cats won today. They beat the Dogtown Dogs 1-0. It was an exciting game. Both teams played hard. The winning goal came in the last minute.

Maria was the hero for the Cats. She zigzagged down the field. She ran around the Dogs' defense. She passed the ball back and forth with her teammates. Then, she got her chance. She kicked the ball. It went in the goal.

It was a great game today. The big winner was girls' soccer. The stands were full. Better luck next time, Dog fans!

How well did you read? Circle your answer.

Directions: Follow the Teacher's Lesson Guide directions each day of the week. At the end of the week, students circle the face showing how well they read.

Examples

Circle.

movement

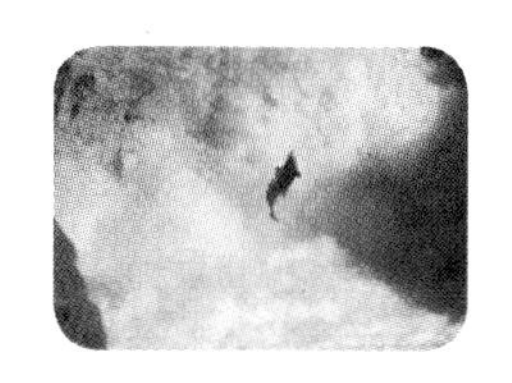

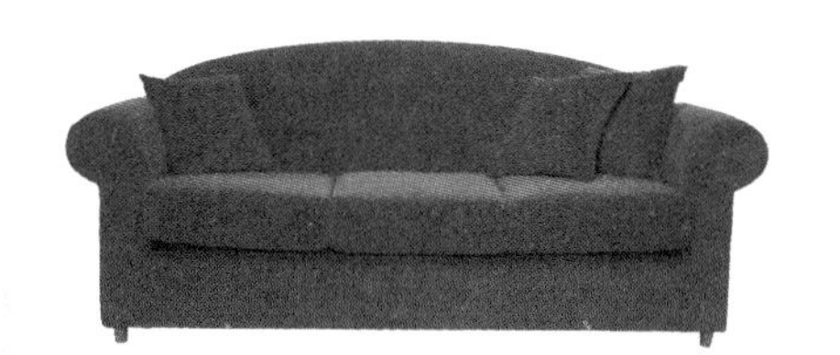

suddenly

It starts raining.

A tree grows.

A turtle walks.

Lightning flashes.

A cat jumps.

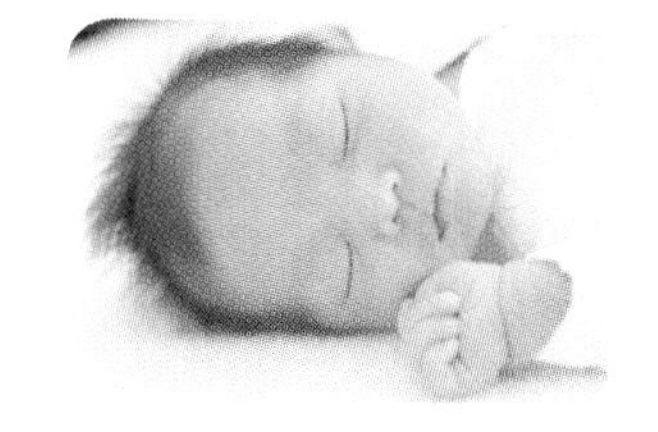
A baby grows.

Directions: Students circle photos showing *movement* and things that happen *suddenly*.

Matching

Match each *movement* word with a picture.

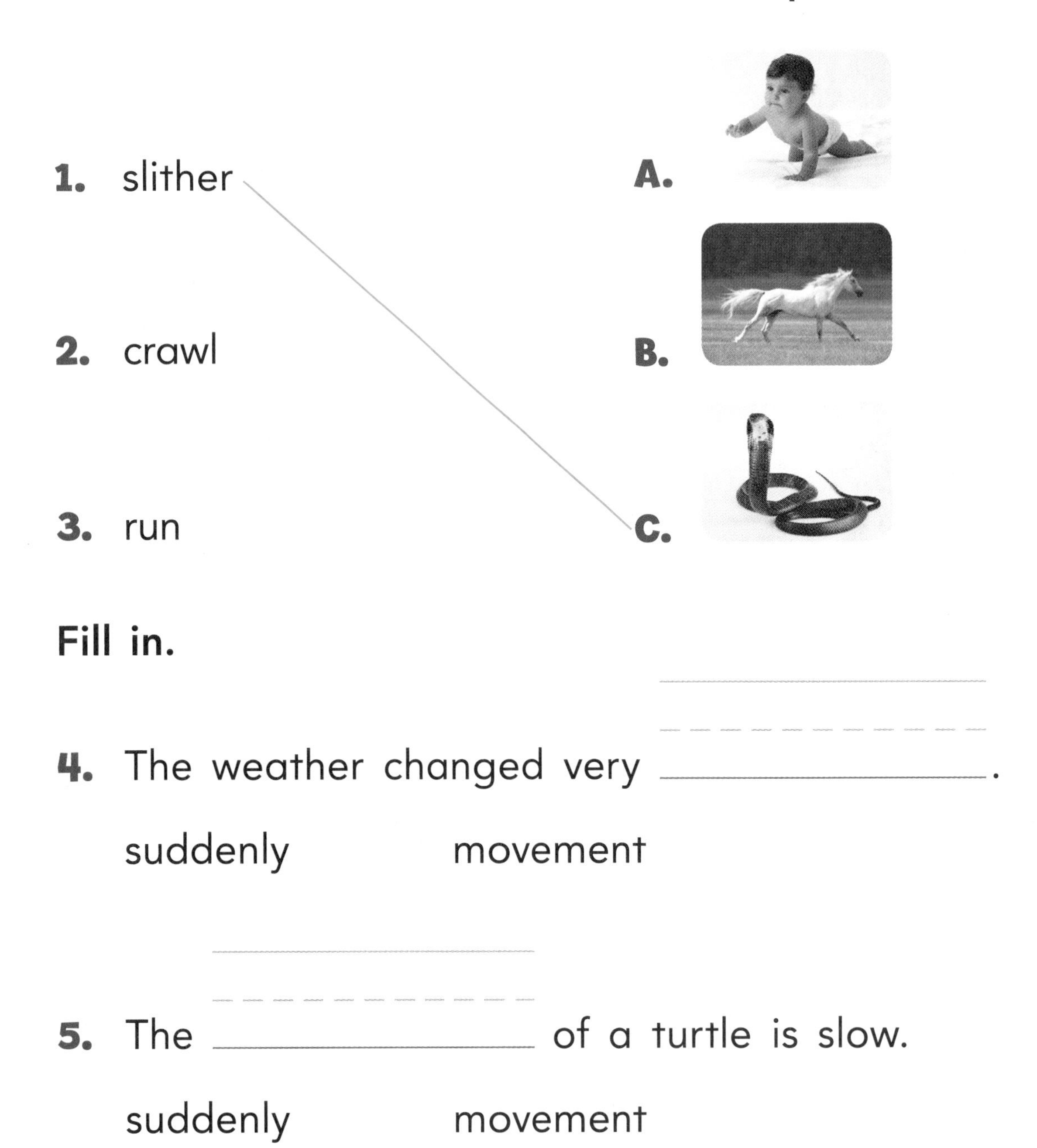

1. slither
2. crawl
3. run

A.
B.
C.

Fill in.

4. The weather changed very ______________.

suddenly movement

5. The ______________ of a turtle is slow.

suddenly movement

Directions: At the top of the page, students match each movement to the best picture. On the bottom of the page, read the sentences and have students circle the best word for each sentence.

Short *u*

hug	bus	cut	gum	was
rub	cub	duck	plum	but

Write the word.

1. bus

2.  ____________

3.  ____________

4.  ____________

5.  ____________

6. ____________

7. I fell and ____________ my elbow.

8. I ____________ lotion on my arm.

9. It ____________ cold outside.

10. It was warm ____________ windy.

Directions: Review the spelling words. Have students write each word.

Make Predictions

Making predictions is making guesses about what will happen next.

1. This looks like mom is pouring juice.
2. What do I think will happen next?

Read. Make a prediction.

Carmen wanted a cold snack.
Mom put juice in the ice cube tray.
Then Carmen put the tray in
the freezer.

What will happen to the juice?

It will freeze.

The juice froze. Now Carmen
has an icy treat!

Was your prediction correct? Circle. (Yes) **No**

Read. Make a prediction.

Today is Dad's birthday. Nicki wants to do something for him.

"I know! Mom, can I have paper and glue and scissors?"

What will Nicki make for Dad?

Nicki cuts out nice pictures and puts them on the card. Then she writes "Happy Birthday." She knows Dad will like this card!

Was your prediction correct? Circle. Yes No

Directions: Read the text on page 72. Ask what will happen. Then finish reading and confirm that the prediction was correct. Repeat for page 73. Have students make a prediction. Continue reading and have students check their predictions.

Use a Dictionary

A **dictionary**

- tells you the meaning of a word
- lists words in ABC order

Look at the dictionary. Answer the questions.

thirsty the feeling that you want to drink something

top the highest part of something
tree a large plant with one trunk

What word comes after top?

thirsty   tree

Write the definition of top.

Look at the dictionary. Answer the questions.

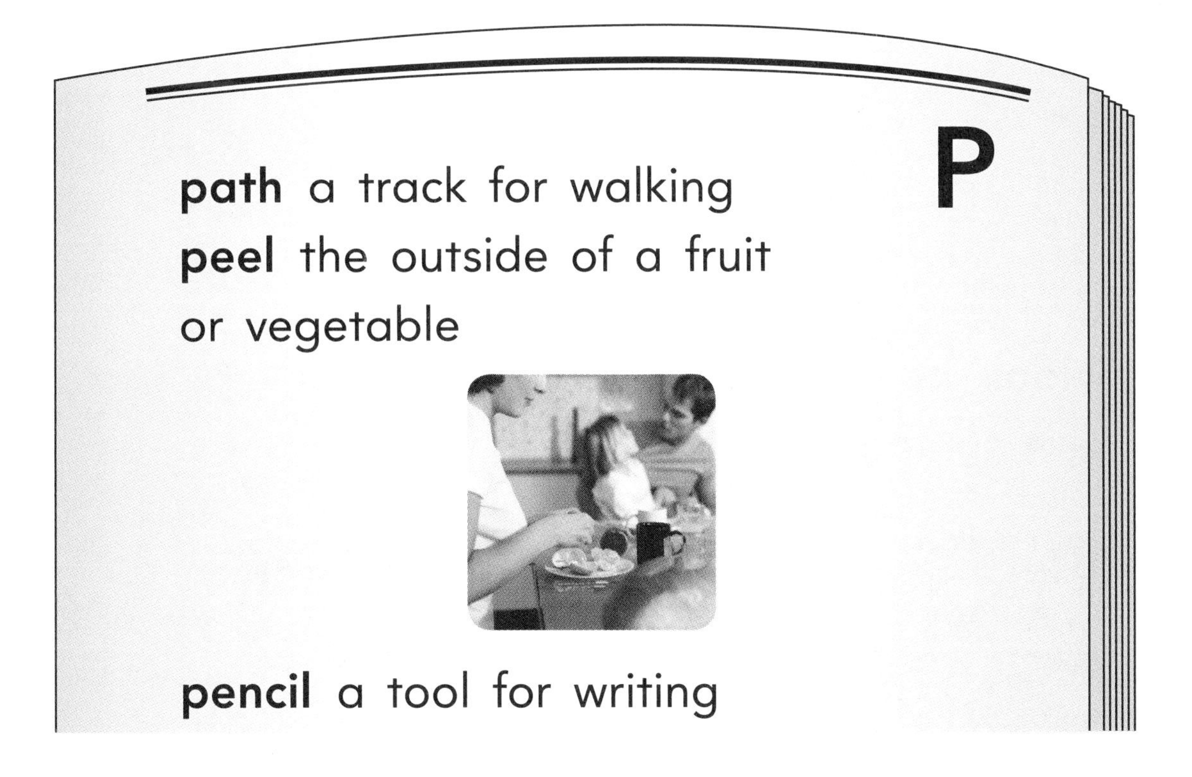

P

path a track for walking
peel the outside of a fruit or vegetable
pencil a tool for writing

What word comes before peel?

pencil path

Write the definition of path.

____

Directions: Students look at the entry and the questions on page 74. Then they answer the questions about the entries on page 75.

Sequence Events

The **sequence** tells the order that things happen in.

1 → 2 → 3 → 4

Listen and look at the pictures. Write numbers next to the pictures.

A storm is coming.

The family has a picnic.

The family hikes outside.

The family drives home.

Directions: Students look at the pictures. Read the story: *One day, a family was hiking together outside. They stopped for a picnic. They were having fun, but soon the sky got dark and very cloudy. "Let's go," said Dad. "I think a storm is coming. It's going to rain." They drove home. But they still had fun at home!* Help students write a number for each sentence to show the order of events.

Special Nouns

Common nouns tell the name of people, places or things.

Proper nouns tell the name of a specific person, place or thing. Proper nouns begin with capital letters.

	Common Noun	Proper Noun
	This is a girl.	This is Maria.

Write the proper nouns.

Mrs. Jones   Main Street   Texas   Jack

1. teacher Mrs. Jones
2. friend
3. street

Directions: Review common and proper nouns. Then have students rewrite the sentences with a proper noun from the box.

Investigation Sheet

1. My Books

2. What I Learned

Directions: Read each numbered item to students. Students write the book titles that they used to collect information for the Inquiry Question. Then they draw and write what they learned from the books.

Taking Tests

Here is a question about *Desert Wonders:*

From the information on pages 8–9, what can you tell about the saguaro cactus? (Page 8)

Ⓐ It lives in the Grand Canyon.
Ⓑ It doesn't get very tall.
Ⓒ It starts as an egg.
Ⓓ It grows very slowly.

What is the question asking for? What you can tell about the saguaro cactus?

- Does the saguaro cactus live in the Grand Canyon? No, it lives in the Sonoran Desert.
- Is it true the saguaro cactus doesn't get very tall? No, the saguaro gets very tall.
- Does the saguaro cactus start as an egg? No, it starts as a seed.
- Does the saguaro cactus grow slowly? Yes, it does. D is the correct answer.

Look at the questions on the next page.

Directions: With the Concepts Big Book open, work through both pages of Taking Tests with students. Remind them to pay attention to the directions, especially key words that tell how to answer the question.

Taking Tests

Look at each answer choice. Is it the right answer to the question? Why or why not?

1. Which shows the correct order of steps in a butterfly's life? (Page 11)

Ⓐ caterpillar, butterfly, chrysalis, egg
Ⓑ butterfly, caterpillar, egg, chrysalis
Ⓒ egg, caterpillar, chrysalis, butterfly
Ⓓ egg, chrysalis, caterpillar, butterfly

2. Which is the most important idea on page 28? (Page 28)

Ⓐ Animals in the desert change.
Ⓑ The weather changes quickly in the desert.
Ⓒ Animals move to find water in the desert.
Ⓓ The desert is full of change and movement.

3. From the information on pages 18–21, what can you tell about a flash flood?

Ⓐ Flash floods cause the river to rise slowly.
Ⓑ Flash floods happen suddenly.
Ⓒ Flash floods happen all the time.
Ⓓ Flash floods cause lightning.

My Weekly Planner

Week of	
Theme Vocabulary	
Differentiated Vocabulary	
Comprehension Strategy and Skill	Strategy: Skill:
Vocabulary Strategy	
Spelling Skill	
Fluency	Selection:
Writing and Language Arts	Writing form:
Grammar	Grammar skill:

Play

Read this play aloud.

The Sun and The Wind

by Harley Madison

Wind: I can make hurricanes. What can you do?

Sun: I'll show you. I can get this boy to take his coat off, and you can't.

Wind: We'll see about that!

Narrator: Wind blew. The boy closed his coat.

Sun: Now it's my turn.

Narrator: Sun shone brightly. The boy opened his coat.

Sun: Just wait.

Narrator: Soon the boy took his coat off.

Wind: OK, Sun, I guess you are stronger.

How well did you read? Circle your answer.

Directions: Use the Teacher's Lesson Guide for directions on fluency practice and evaluation.

Sentences

Circle the correct word.

1. 

The dog ______ me home.

followed **arrived**

2. 

We ______ home at 4:30.

followed **arrived**

3. 

She ______ at the airport.

followed **arrived**

4. 

We ______ our teacher to the playground.

followed **arrived**

Directions: Read each sentence aloud. Students circle the correct vocabulary word.

Examples

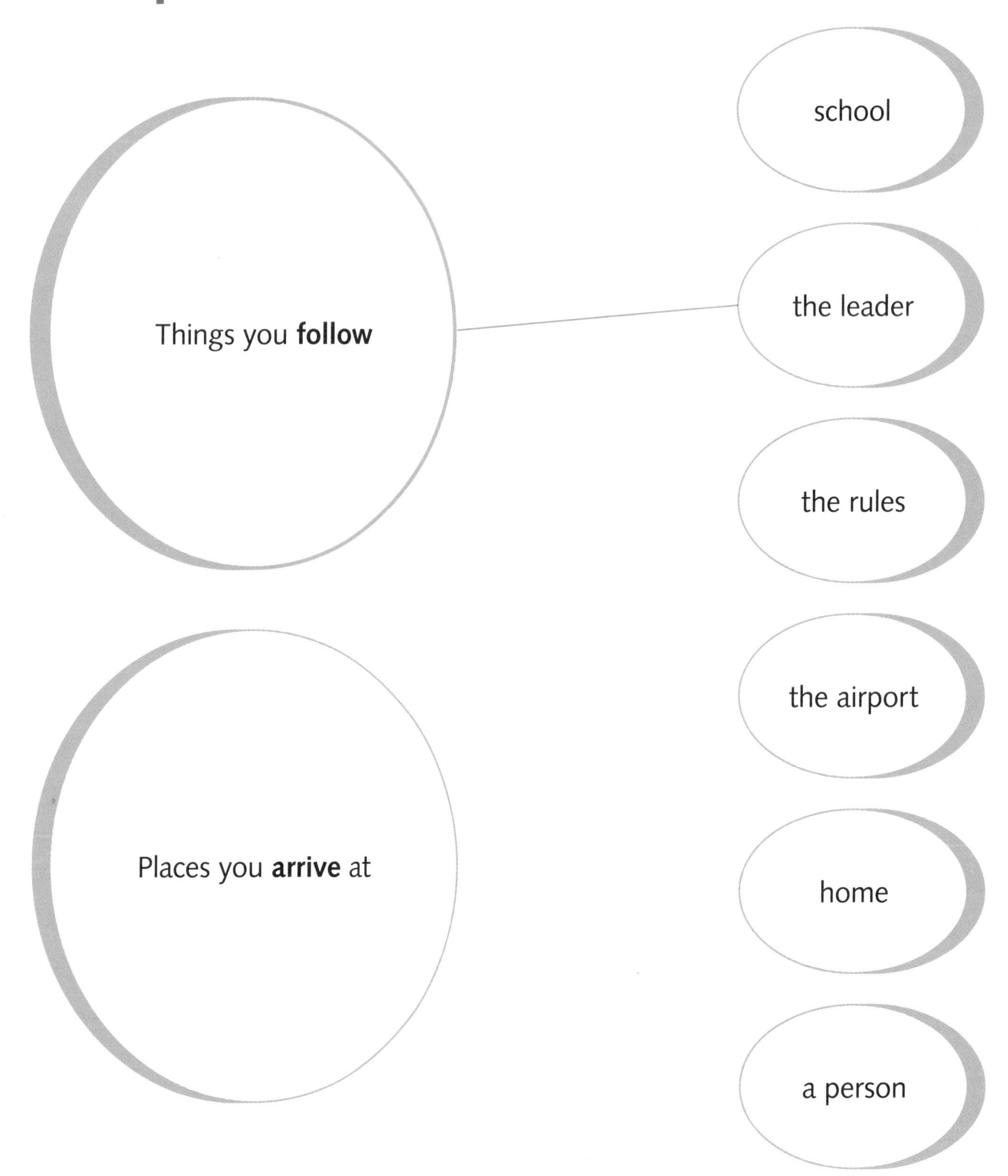

Directions: Students draw lines from the vocabulary words on the left to match the words and phrases on the right.

Beginning *r* Blends

crack	drop	grab	trick	brother
scrub	grin	drum	strip	pretty

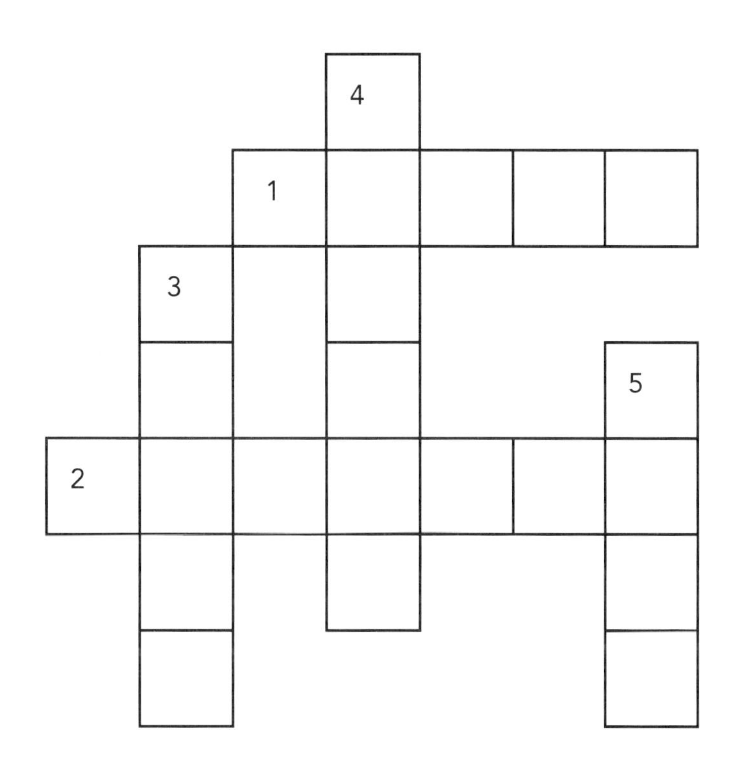

ACROSS

1. a line where something is broken

2. a boy in a family

DOWN

3. to rub hard

4. nice to look at

5. to let fall

Directions: Review the spelling words. Read the clues for the crossword puzzle. Help students write each word in the puzzle.

Summarize

- A summary tells the most important ideas.
- Use your own words to **summarize**.

Look at the pictures. Read.

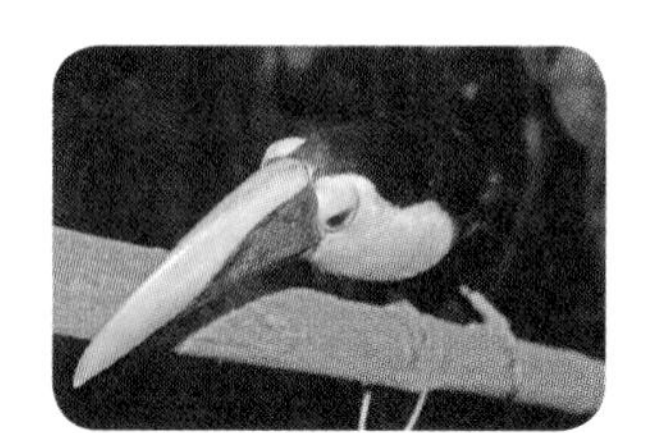

The zoo is a great place to see all kinds of animals. There are animals from the desert, like snakes and lizards. There are animals that swim, like frogs and seals. There are also animals that fly, like birds and bats.

Write the most important ideas. Write a summary.

Important ideas	• There are many animals at the zoo. • Some animals live in the desert. • Some animals fly or swim.
Summary	The zoo has many animals. Some live in the desert. Some swim. Some fly.

Look at the picture. Read.

There was a big storm last night. The wind blew hard. Lightning flashed. The wind broke branches off the trees. Everywhere was a mess. Today we worked together to clean up the mess.

Write the most important ideas. Write a summary.

Important ideas	• There was a storm.
Summary	

Directions: Discuss the text on page 86. Then read the text on page 87. Help students fill in the boxes with the important ideas and a summary.

Descriptive Language

- Use words that describe things.
- Create a picture in your mind as you read.

cold, clear ice

fuzzy, yellow duckling

sweet, juicy orange

old, tall cactus

big, bright fireworks

Underline.

1. The bright, red apples hung on the tree.

2. I picked a big apple.

3. It was round and smooth in my hands.

4. It smelled fresh.

5. It tasted sweet and juicy.

Directions: Point out the photographs on page 88 and read aloud the descriptive words. Encourage students to use their own words to describe each picture. Then read the sentences describing an apple on page 89. Students underline the descriptive language in each sentence.

Figurative Language

Draw.

1. The tree was as tall as a house.

2. The light was as bright as the sun.

Directions: Students picture each sentence and draw what they see when they listen to the words.

Read and Respond

Think about *An Orange in January*. Answer the questions.

1. What did you like best about the story?

2. What was surprising about the journey the orange took?

3. What are some words in the story that help you make a picture in your mind of something?

Directions: Students answer the questions to respond to *An Orange in January.*

Identify Details and Facts

Details and facts tell about important ideas.

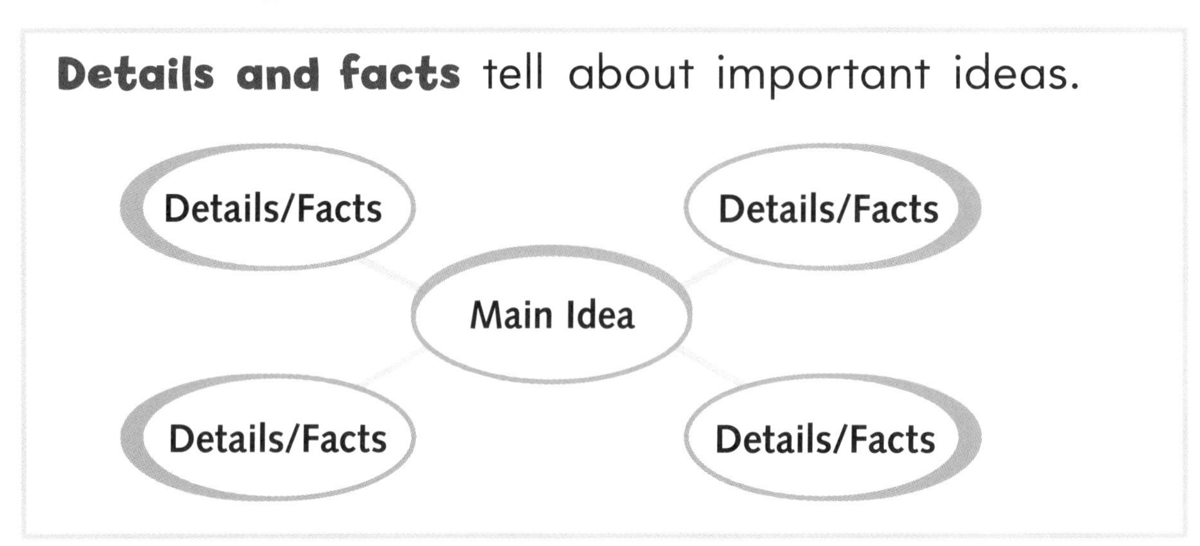

Read. Write details and facts.

Canada geese fly south when it gets cold. They fly over hills and rivers. They fly in a shape like a V. They honk. They fly quickly. They can fly up to 450 miles in one day!

Main Idea:	Geese fly south.
Detail:	
Detail:	
Detail:	

Directions: Read the paragraph on Canada geese. Help students identify details and facts in the text to complete the graphic organizer.

Special Titles

Add titles to names for particular people. You capitalize the short form of the title and add a period.

Mr. Thompson and **Mrs.** Thompson

Dr. Reyna

Ms. Chen

Write the abbreviation.

1. 

_____ Carson

2. 

_____ Springer

3. 

_____ Silva

_____ Silva

Picture Book

What is a picture book?

- A picture book tells a story or explains an idea.
- It uses drawings or pictures.
- It uses words to help tell the story.
- It has a cover with a title and an author.

Directions: Read the headings and each bulleted phrase to students. Have students study the example of the picture book. Students use this information to help them create a picture book to share their Inquiry findings.

My Weekly Planner

Week of	
Theme Vocabulary	
Differentiated Vocabulary	
Comprehension Strategy and Skill	Strategy: Skill:
Vocabulary Strategy	
Spelling Skill	
Fluency	Selection:
Writing and Language Arts	Writing form:
Grammar	Grammar skill:

Riddle

Read this riddle aloud.

What Am I?

by Morgan Steiner

I have three states.
But I am not a place.

I can be hard and slippery.
But if I get warm,
I will change.

I can be drippy and splashy.
But if I get very hot, I will change again.

I can be hot and steamy.
But if I cool off, I will change again.

What am I?

How well did you read? Circle your answer.

Directions: Follow the Teacher's Lesson Guide directions each day of the week. At the end of the week, students circle the face showing how well they read.

Sentences

measured	enormous	arrived
movement	suddenly	followed

Use the words to complete the sentences.

The plane arrived ______ at noon.

The cat saw ______ in the grass.

The door opened ______.

The dog ______ me home.

I ______ the table with a ruler.

The whale is ______.

Directions: Tell students to use vocabulary words to complete the sentences.

Word Pairs

Complete the sentences.

measured/ruler	enormous/animal	arrived/teacher
movement/slow	suddenly/rain	followed/snake

1. ______________________, it began to

______________________.

2. An elephant is an ______________________

______________________.

3. The ______________________

______________________ early.

Directions: Have students work in pairs to choose words to complete sentences.

Short *e*

yes	men	fell	jet	then
leg	neck	step	bed	end

Write a letter in each blank to spell three new words.

Directions: Tell students that one spelling word fits in each horizontal line of squares. If the puzzle is completed correctly, the word in each shaded box will match the picture.

Summarize

- A summary tells the most important ideas.
- Use your own words to **summarize**.

Look at the picture. Read.

My puppy and I do a lot of things together. I walk with him. I play with him. He is my friend.

Write the most important ideas. Then write a summary.

Important Ideas

- The boy and his puppy do things together.
- He walks and plays with the puppy.
- They are friends.

Summary

The boy and his puppy are friends. They walk and play together.

Look at the picture. Read.

The children get on the roller coaster. The roller coaster slowly crawls up a hill. Then it rolls down fast. It zigzags. It is a lot of fun to ride!

Write the most important ideas. Write a summary.

Important Ideas

- The children get on a roller coaster.
-
-

Summary

Directions: Read the text on page 100. Then read the text on page 101. Help students fill in the graphic organizer with the important ideas and a summary.

Use Multiple Strategies

Remember that you can use vocabulary strategies to help you figure out the meaning of words.

Vocabulary strategies

- Descriptive language tells how something looks, feels, smells, or sounds.
- Look for context clues before and after a word to help with its meaning.
- Use dictionaries or other resources to find the meaning of a word.

Look at the describing words.

slippery, wet fish

Look for the context clues.

The dog is lost. He is missing.

Write two descriptive words.

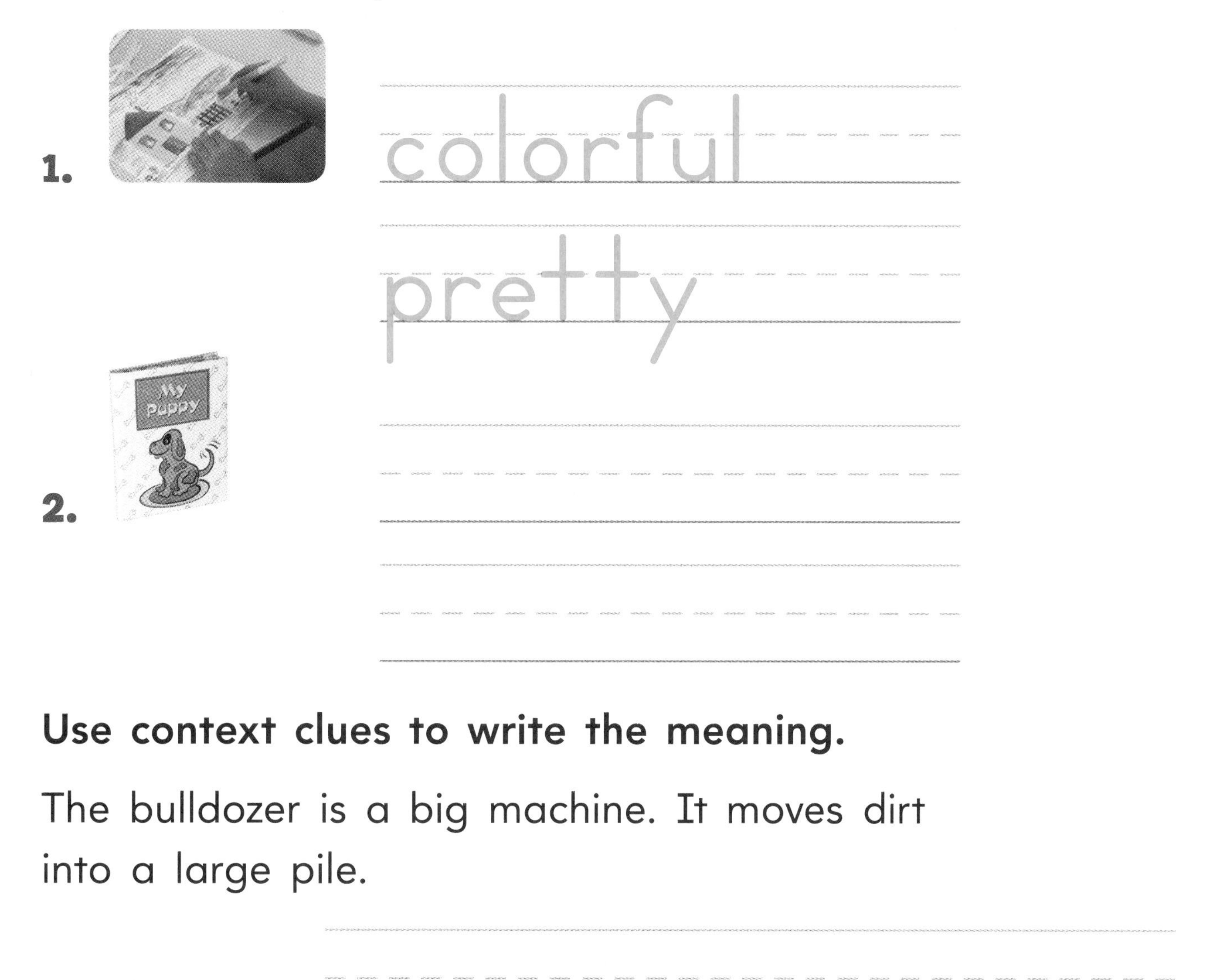

Use context clues to write the meaning.

The bulldozer is a big machine. It moves dirt into a large pile.

A bulldozer is ______________________________

Directions: Students write two words to describe each picture. Then they use the context clues to find the meaning of *bulldozer.* Remind students to use a dictionary if they still need help with the meaning of the word.

Details and Facts

Details and facts tell more about important ideas in a text.

Details — Facts — Main Idea — Facts — Details

Read. Answer the questions.

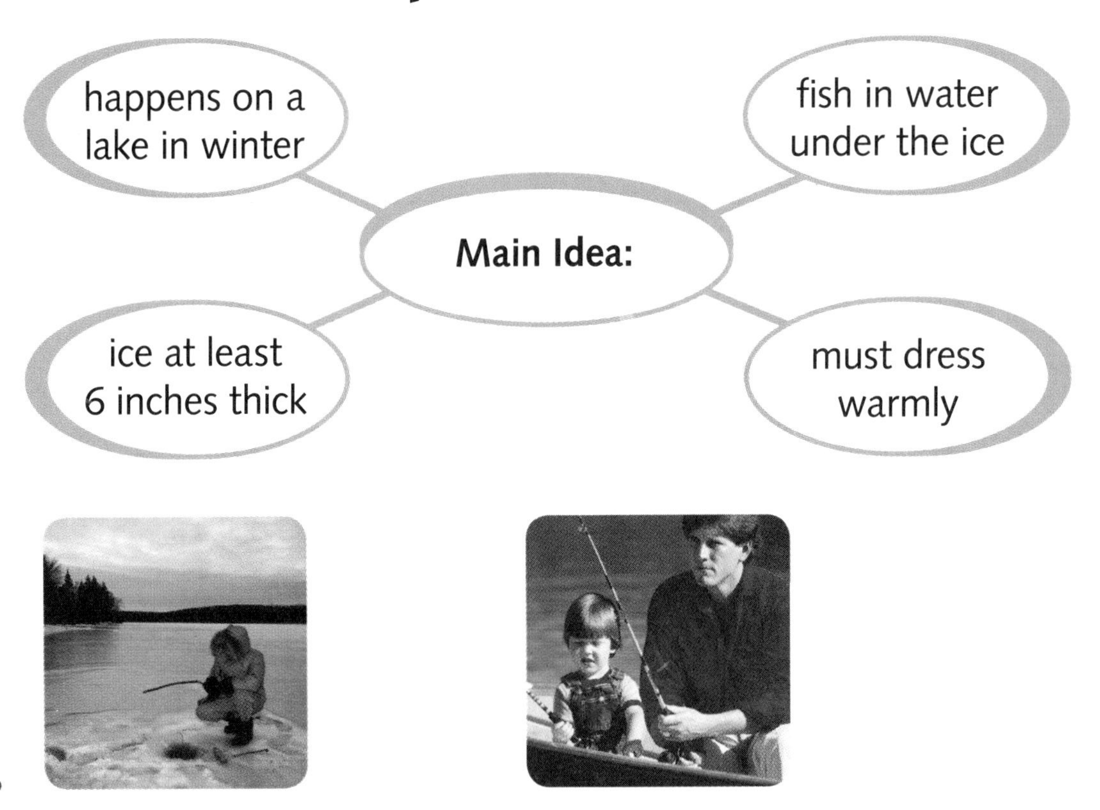

1\.

2\. **Fishing in Summer** **Fishing in Winter**

Directions: Read the graphic organizer together. Have students answer the questions. *1. Circle the picture that best illustrates the details and facts on the chart. 2. Circle the words that belong in the circle labeled "Main Idea."*

Days, Months, Holidays, Cities, States

The names of days of the week, months, holidays, cities, and states are special nouns. They begin with capital letters.

day	Monday
month	June
holiday	Thankgiving Day
city and state	Miami, Florida

Write the sentences correctly.

1. october 31 is halloween.

2. Today is friday, march 1.

3. I live in dallas, texas.

Investigation Sheet

1. My Books

2. What I Learned

Directions: Read each numbered item to students. Students write the book titles that they used to collect information for the Inquiry Question. Then they draw and write what they learned from the books.

Taking Tests

Here is a question about *An Orange in January.*

Where does the orange begin its journey? Where does it go?

How can you answer this question? First, find out where the orange begins its trip. Then, find out where the orange goes. Finally, find out where it is at the end.

Beginning

- grows on tree

Middle

- is picked
- goes to a store

End

- boy buys it
- boy takes it to school

Directions: With the literature book open, work through both pages of Taking Tests with students. Remind them to pay attention to the directions, especially key words that tell how to answer the question.

Taking Tests

Here is another question about *An Orange in January:*

How does the orange change from a flower to a fruit?

Write your ideas in the organizer.

Beginning

-

Middle

-
-

End

-
-

My Weekly Planner

Week of	
Theme Vocabulary	
Differentiated Vocabulary	
Comprehension Strategy and Skill	Strategy: Skill:
Vocabulary Strategy	
Spelling Skill	
Fluency	Selection:
Writing and Language Arts	Writing form:
Grammar	Grammar skill:

Poem

Read this poem aloud.

Town and City

by Cass Algren

In my town, I walk up and down.
In my town, I ride up and down.
In my town, I go all around.
Would you like to live in my town?

In my city, the nights are pretty.
In my city, the lights are pretty.
In my city, the streets are busy.
Would you like to live in my city?

How well did you read? Circle your answer.

Directions: Follow the Teacher's Lesson Guide directions each day of the week. At the end of the week, students circle the face showing how well they read.

Examples

Who are your neighbors? Write.

Mrs. Lopez

What places are nearby? Write.

Fern Park

Directions: Have students brainstorm people and places in or near their neighborhood.

Mini-Book

neighbors	nearby	close	people
places	far	across	street

Draw and write about where you live.

Where I Live

by

Directions: Students draw pictures and write in the mini-book, telling about the people and places in their neighborhood. Remind students that they can use the word bank above to help them write.

Final Blends

sand	jump	tent	lamp	next
milk	help	went	desk	want

Write two letters to finish each word.

1. s a n d
2. n e __ __
3. t e __ __
4. h e __ __
5. d e __ __
6. w e __ __
7. m i __ __
8. l a __ __
9. j u __ __
10. w a __ __

Directions: Review the spelling words. Students write two letters to finish each word.

Ask and Answer Questions

- **Ask questions** before you read.
- When you read, look for clues to **answer** your questions.

Clues

title text pictures captions

Question	In the Book	Answer
Ask a question about the story.	**Text** Read the title, text, and captions. **Pictures** Look at the pictures.	Try to **answer** your question.

Look at the pages. Write.

The Outdoor Market

We like the market.
Farmers sell
berries and flowers.

Read. Finish the chart.

Question	In the Book	Answer
What can you buy at the outdoor market?	Text Pictures	

Directions: Students look at the pages of the book. Remind students that the answers to questions can sometimes be found in the text or in the pictures. Read the text with students and have them fill out the "In the Book" and "Answer" columns.

Use Picture Clues

Sometimes **pictures** help you understand a word you do not know.

Read and circle the picture clues. Answer the question.

She wanted to get a book about unicorns.

From the picture, I can tell that a unicorn is

an animal that looks like a dog with big ears

or

an animal that looks like a horse with a horn

Read and circle the picture clues.
Answer the question.

1. Meet me in the field at five o'clock.

From the picture clues, I can tell that a field is

an open grassy place

or

a kind of house

2. On Sunday, we went to town.

From the picture clues, I can tell that a town is

a place with people and stores

or

a place with cows and sheep

Directions: Review with students the example on page 116. On page 117, students circle picture clues that tell about the underlined words. Then students circle the best meaning of each underlined word.

Fact and Opinion

Fact: information that can be proved

Bakers use flour to make bread.

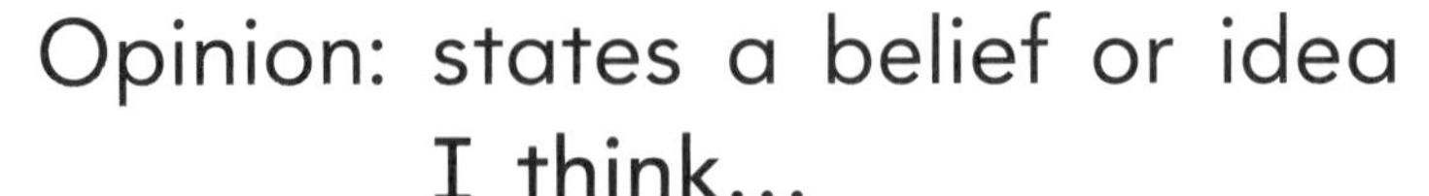

Opinion: states a belief or idea
I think...
I believe...

I think bread is delicious.

Write **F** for a fact or **O** for an opinion.

1. F ______ Doctors work with people who are sick.

   O ______ I think doctors have the most important job.

2. ______ The museum opens at 10.

   ______ I think the museum is interesting.

Directions: Tell students that in each sentence pair, there is one fact and one opinion. Students write **F** for **fact** or **O** for **opinion** next to each sentence.

Nouns as Subjects

The **subject** of a sentence tells who or what the sentence is about. The main word in a subject is a **noun**.

The baby talks. **My mother smiles.**

Read the sentence. Look for the main word in the subject. Circle this noun.

1.  The students like the story.

2.  The big lion sleeps a lot.

3.  My new bike is fun to ride.

4.  Mr. Ortiz lives next door to us.

Directions: Remind students that a noun is a word that names a person, place, or thing. Read the sentences aloud. Have students find the noun within the subject and circle it.

Mural

What is a mural?

- A mural is a large picture on a wall.
- A mural shows more than one thing.
- Artists draw, paint, or use other things to make a mural.
- Murals can share an idea or tell a story.
- Murals are in a place for everyone to see.

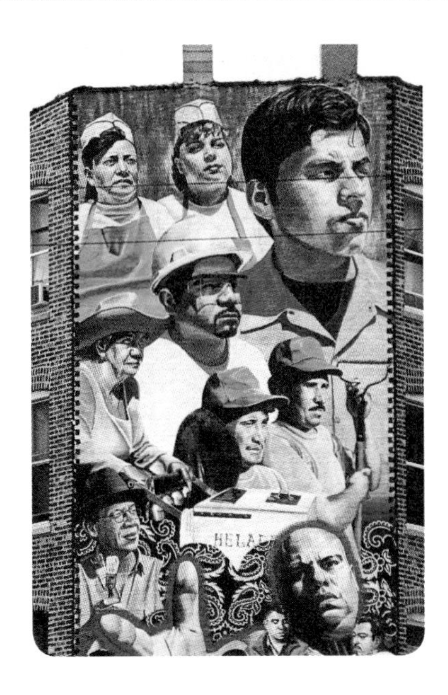

Directions: Read the headings and each bulleted phrase to students. Have students study the examples of murals. Students use this information to help them create a mural to share their Inquiry findings.

My Weekly Planner

Week of ____________________

Theme Vocabulary

Differentiated Vocabulary

Comprehension Strategy and Skill

Strategy: ____________________

Skill: ____________________

Vocabulary Strategy

Spelling Skill

Fluency

Selection:

Writing and Language Arts

Writing form:

Grammar

Grammar skill:

Play

Read this play aloud.

Career Day

by Arnie Goodman

Students: What does
a police officer do?
Police Officer: I make sure
you follow rules.
Call me if you need help.

Students: What does a nurse do?
Nurse: I help you when you are sick.
Call me if you don't feel well.

Student: What does a fire fighter do?
Fire Fighter: I help put out fires.
Call me if you smell smoke.

How well did you read? Circle your answer.

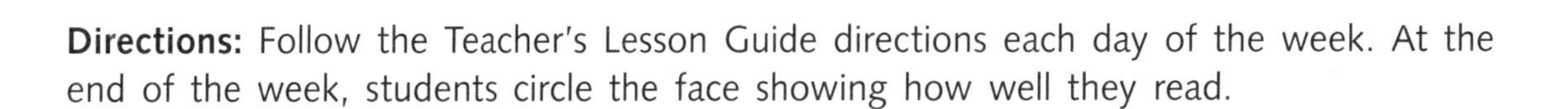

Directions: Follow the Teacher's Lesson Guide directions each day of the week. At the end of the week, students circle the face showing how well they read.

Examples

Circle things that are entertaining.

Draw lines between the choices. Circle your choice.

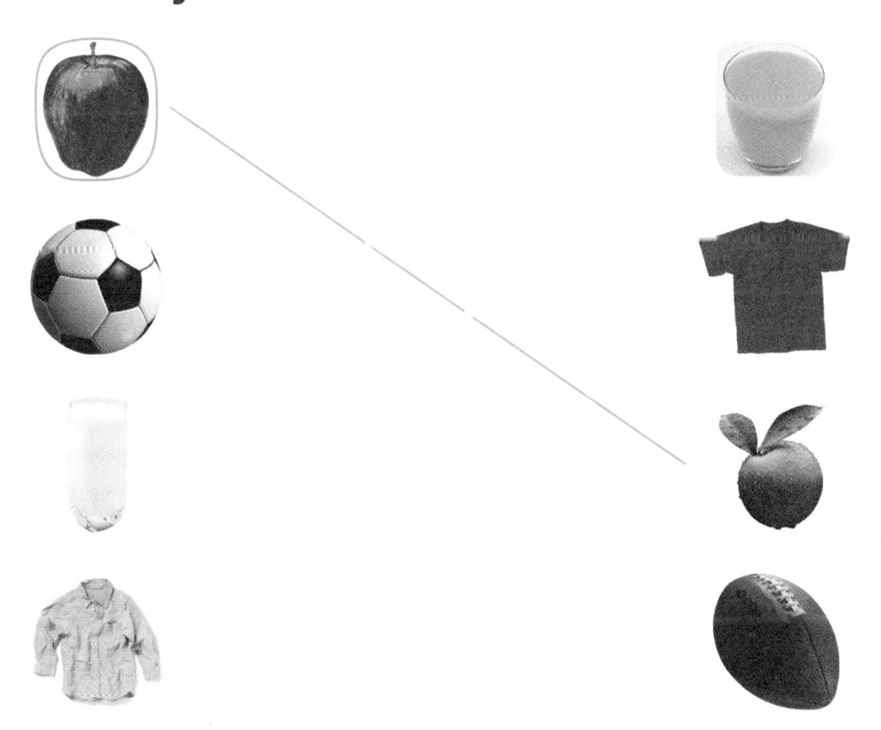

Directions: On the top of the page, students circle the things that are **entertaining**. On the bottom of the page, students draw lines between the pairs of things that could be **choices**. Then students circle the thing they would choose.

Idea Completion

Complete each sentence.

1. If you gave someone **choices,** you might say,
"Pick one."

2. If something is **entertaining,** it is
____________________.

3. When you watch something **entertaining,**
you might ____________________.

4. If the class had to make a **choice** together,
the teacher might ____________________
____________________.

5. If it is hard to make a **choice,** you could
____
____________________.

Directions: Read the sentence starters. Help students complete each sentence.

Words with *sh* and *th*

ship	shell	fish	trash	when
this	path	bath	that	thank

Across

3. "What time?"
4. ________ you very much!
5. a trail you walk on
6. garbage

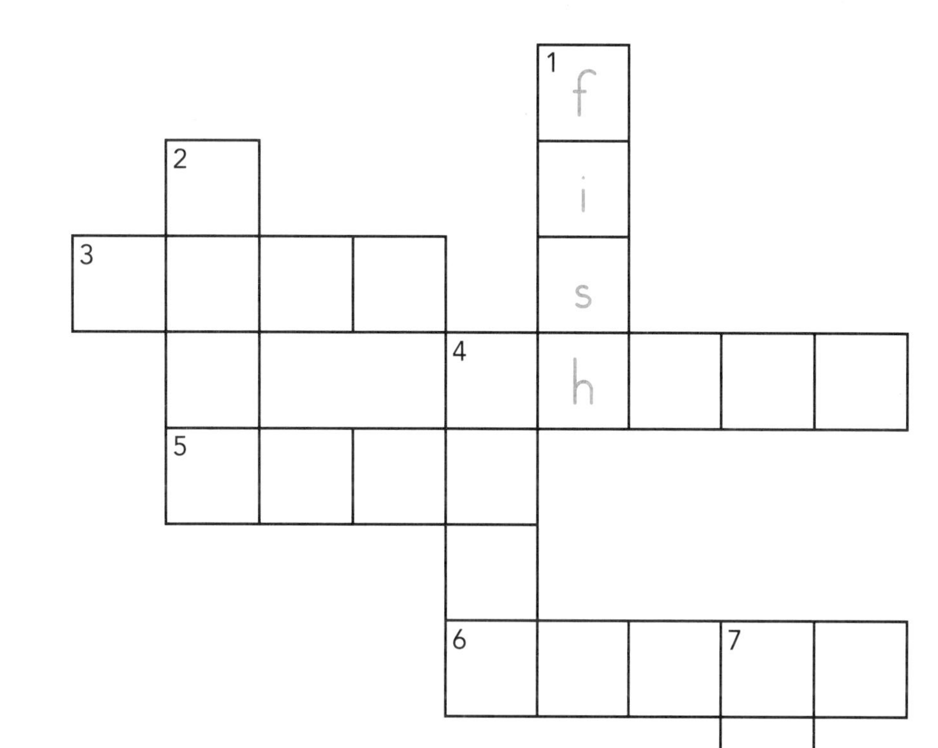

Down

1. an animal that swims
2. a large boat
4. not *this*, but ________
7. something you find on a beach

Circle the words that were not used in the puzzle.

Directions: Have students complete the puzzle and circle the words that are left.

Ask and Answer Questions

As you read, you can **ask questions**.

You can also **answer** your question.

To answer a question, think about what you already know or keep reading.

Ally is here to play with her friend Beth.

What would you ask about this story?

Why is Ally alone?

What do you already know?

I play with friends.

Read.

Where is Beth? She must not be here.

Now what do you know?

Beth is not there.

This police officer has a very important job.

What would you ask about this story?

What do you already know?

Read.

He stops the cars so people can cross the street. He keeps people safe.

Now what do you know?

Directions: Remind students that they can ask questions as they read. Help them read the items. They ask and answer questions.

Use a Dictionary

A **dictionary**

- tells you the meaning of a word
- lists words in ABC order

Look at the dictionary. Answer the questions.

C

choice something you can pick or choose

circle a round shape
city a big or important town
clay a kind of dirt for making pots

What does choice mean?

a big or important town | something you can pick

What word comes after city?

clay | choice

What is a circle?

a round shape | a kind of dirt

Look at the dictionary. Answer the questions.

hat something you wear to cover your head

hatch to break out of an egg

hay dried grass used as food for animals

heal to get better

What word comes before hatch?

hay | hat

What is hay?

something you wear on your head | dried grass you feed to animals

What word comes after hay?

heal | hatch

What does heal mean?

to get better | to break out of an egg

Directions: Review the dictionary page on page 128 and the questions. Then read the dictionary page on page 129. Students answer the questions by circling the correct answer.

Fact and Opinion

You can prove a **fact**.

You can tell your beliefs or **opinions**. Other people might think something different.

Circle the fact. Underline the opinion.

1. 

Ice cream is cold.

Chocolate ice cream is the best!

2. 

Soccer is my favorite sport.

A soccer team has eleven players.

3. 

The Earth is round.

I think we should keep the Earth clean.

Directions: Students circle the fact and underline the opinion in each pair of sentences.

Verbs

run	swim	jump	read
throw	tie	fly	sit

Use a verb to describe each picture.

1. 

sit

2. 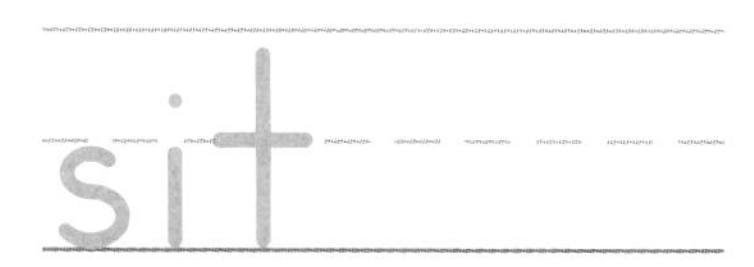

3. 

4. 

5. 

6.

7.

8. 

Directions: Students write an action verb that describes each picture.

Investigation Sheet

1. My Books

2. What I Learned

Directions: Read each numbered item to students. Students write the book titles that they used to collect information for the Inquiry Question. Then they draw and write what they learned from the books.

Taking Tests

Here is a question about *Where People Live:*

What is true about all communities? (page 9)

Ⓐ They all are big cities.
Ⓑ They all have things people need.
Ⓒ They all have tall buildings.
Ⓓ They all have museums.

What is the question about?
It is about how all communities are alike.

- Are all communities big cities?
  No, some communities are small towns.
- Do all communities have things people need?
  Yes, they do. B is the correct answer.
- Do all communities have tall buildings?
  No, small towns might not have tall buildings.
- Do all communities have museums?
  No, not all communities have museums.

Look at the questions on the next page.

Directions: With the Concepts Big Book open, work through both pages of Taking Tests with students. Remind them to pay attention to the directions, especially key words that tell how to answer the question.

Taking Tests

1. Which information is most important? (page 14)

Ⓐ Some communities are fun.
Ⓑ Families like to go shopping.
Ⓒ Firefighters help put out fires.
Ⓓ A community has a post office.

2. Which sentence about Little Rock is an opinion? (page 23)

Ⓐ The Little Rock River Market is fun.
Ⓑ The Museum of Discovery has science activities.
Ⓒ Little Rock is a big city in Arkansas.
Ⓓ Riverfest is a festival in Little Rock.

3. What is something people need? (page 22)

Ⓐ toys
Ⓑ food
Ⓒ games
Ⓓ bicycles

4. Which sentence is a fact? (page 10)

Ⓐ A library is a good place to visit.
Ⓑ A big city is a great place to live.
Ⓒ It is fun to be in a sack race.
Ⓓ Little Rock is a big city in Arkansas.

My Weekly Planner

Week of	
Theme Vocabulary	
Differentiated Vocabulary	
Comprehension Strategy and Skill	Strategy: Skill:
Vocabulary Strategy	
Spelling Skill	
Fluency	Selection:
Writing and Language Arts	Writing form:
Grammar	Grammar skill:

Song

Read this song aloud.

Neighbors Play!

by Pat Blake

Neighbors play with us today!
We can go to the park
and swim in the lake.
We can eat a picnic we make.
We can ride bikes or roller skate.
Neighbors play!

Neighbors play with us today!
We can go to the library.
We can hear a true story.
We can hear one that's funny.
Neighbors play!

How well did you read? Circle your answer.

Directions: Follow the Teacher's Lesson Guide directions each day of the week. At the end of the week, students circle the face showing how well they read.

More Than One Meaning

Right can mean many things.

- correct or true

  Example: He got the **right** answer.

- exactly

  Example: Look **right** here.

- not left

  Example: I can hop on my **right** foot.

Circle the best meaning.

1. The store is on the **right** side of the street.
   correct or true   exactly   not left
2. It is time for lunch **right** now.
   correct or true   exactly   not left
3. No, that is not the **right** answer.
   correct or true   exactly   not left
4. Turn **right** at the corner.
   correct or true   exactly   not left

Directions: Review the different meanings of the word *right*. Then students circle the meaning used in each sentence.

Opposites

Write the words.

true	sort of	exactly
left	correct	wrong

right

Yes	No
true	

Directions: Help students read the words from the word bank. Point out the word **Yes** on the left side of the chart. Explain that the words that mean the same thing as **right** should be written on the this side. Repeat with **No**, explaining that the words that mean the opposite from **right** should be written on the right side.

Words with *ch* and *tch*

chin	chest	chop	such	much
inch	lunch	catch	rich	what

Fill in the blanks.

1. Just below your mouth is your chin.
2. This tiny toy is one ________ long.
3. Did you ever ________ a fish?
4. How ________ does the game cost?
5. This is ________ a big mess!
6. Someone with a lot of money is ________.
7. ________ time is it?
8. Mom uses a knife to ________ carrots.

Directions: Students fill in each blank with a spelling word. Have students circle the words that are left.

Monitor Comprehension

When you read, stop and think.
Do you understand?
If you do not understand, use a fix-up strategy.

Follow these steps.

Step 1 Pause while reading.

Step 2 Think about what you don't understand.

Step 3 Choose a fix-up strategy.

Reread	Read On	Ask for Help

Step 4 Check your understanding again.

Read the story.

John wanted to help his relatives.

Pause your reading. Answer the question.

1. What are you confused about?

I don't understand what the word *relatives* **means.**

Read on.

He mowed Grandmother's yard.
He helped his uncle plant flowers.

John was happy.
He liked to help his family.

Answer the question.

2. What do you understand now?

Relatives are people in your ______________

Directions: Help students read the story and practice the strategy.

Use Synonyms

Synonyms are words that have almost the same meaning.

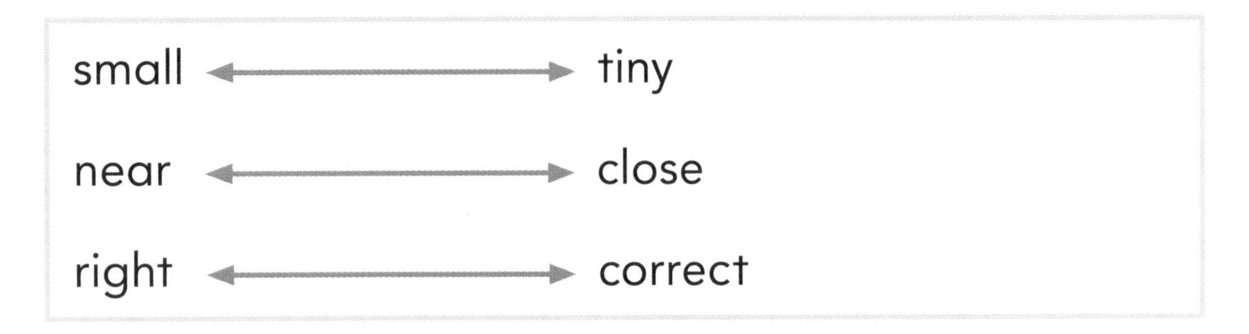

Read the sentences. Circle the synonym.

The line at the ice cream shop was enormous.
It was so big that we didn't want to wait.

What does enormous mean?

1. **Read the sentences. Circle the synonym.**

My clothes got soaked when we washed the car.
They were very wet.

What does soaked mean?

2. **Read the sentences. Circle the synonym.**

My family had a **celebration** on Saturday.
The party was a lot of fun.

What is a celebration?

Directions: Read the sentences on page 142. Point out the synonym *big* and the meaning of *enormous*. Help students complete page 143 in the same way.

Plot

Read the story.

Tasha looked in the mail box. Empty.
"Did you bring in the mail?" she asked
her mom.

"Not I," replied her mom.

"Did you get the mail?" she asked her dad.

"No. Here comes the mailman,"
said her dad.

"Hurrah!" cried Tasha. "A letter from Nana!"

Draw lines to show first, second, and third.

1	The mailbox is empty.
2	Tasha asks for the mail.
3	Tasha gets mail from Nana.

Directions: Help students read the story and draw lines to put the events in order.

Read and Respond

Think about *Where Are You, Boots?* Answer the questions.

1. What did you like best about the story?

2. What was the funniest part of the story?

3. Were you happy with the ending? Why or why not?

Directions: Students answer the questions in response to reading *Where Are You, Boots?*

Recall and Retell

Recall
the most important events in the story.

and

Retell
the story in your own words.

Read the story and retell.

Beginning	Billy and his mom took a subway train.
Middle	They got off the train. They got on a bus.
End	They went to a park. There was a festival.

Directions: Remind students that when they retell a story, they recall it and tell it in their own words. Help students read the story map and then students retell the story to a partner orally. Then students retell it in writing.

Verbs in Sentences

The subject of a sentence tells who or what it is about.

The rest of the sentence tells what the subject does.

The baby **drinks milk.**

Mrs. Gonzales **sings.**

Read the sentence. Then circle the action verb.

1.  My uncle (plays) many songs.

2.  My cousins dance.

3.  My friend Ben walks to school.

4.  Our dog plays fetch with a ball.

Directions: Read the sentences aloud. Have students name the subject. Then have them say what the subject does and circle the action verb.

Puppet Show

What is a puppet show?

- A puppet show is a short play or skit.
- Puppet shows tell a story on a stage.
- The characters are puppets.
- Actors move the puppets and make them talk.
- The actors are not seen.

Directions: Read the headings and each bulleted phrase to students. Have students study the example of the puppet show. Students use this information to help them create a puppet show to share their Inquiry findings.

My Weekly Planner

Week of	
Theme Vocabulary	
Differentiated Vocabulary	
Comprehension Strategy and Skill	Strategy: Skill:
Vocabulary Strategy	
Spelling Skill	
Fluency	Selection:
Writing and Language Arts	Writing form:
Grammar	Grammar skill:

Riddle

Read this riddle aloud.

Can You Guess?

by Joey Lamberger

Can you guess where I am?

I see apples and oranges, but it isn't a tree.
I see fish and shrimp, but it isn't the sea.
I see fruit and potatoes and even some steak.
Here you buy foods to boil, grill, and bake.

My mother picks items to add to the cart.
We choose many foods that are healthy and smart.
When we get home, we'll cook. I can't wait to start!
And then we'll have dinner. That's my favorite part.

Can you guess where I am?

How well did you read? Circle your answer.

Directions: Use the Teacher's Lesson Guide for directions on fluency practice and evaluation.

Connect Words

Circle the correct words.

1. The **neighbors** live ________________.
   far away　　next door　　in my house

2. The ________________ was very **entertaining**.
   clown　　homework　　telephone

3. The store is **nearby**. It is ________________.
   in the next city　　down the street　　in another state

4. 1 + 1 = ________________. That is the **right** answer.
   3　　1　　2

5. We had to make a **choice**. We ________________.
   picked the best one　　went home　　did not choose

Directions: Students circle the words that make sense in the sentence.

Word Sort

close	correct	pick	near	people
funny	laugh	choose	street	true

Sort the words.

neighbors	nearby	entertaining
people		

choices	right

Directions: Have students sort the related words into the five groups. Ask students to tell how and why they sorted the words the way they did.

Words with *ar* and *or*

car	arm	dark	star	your
corn	sort	fork	horn	are

Write a spelling word in each row.

What is this animal?

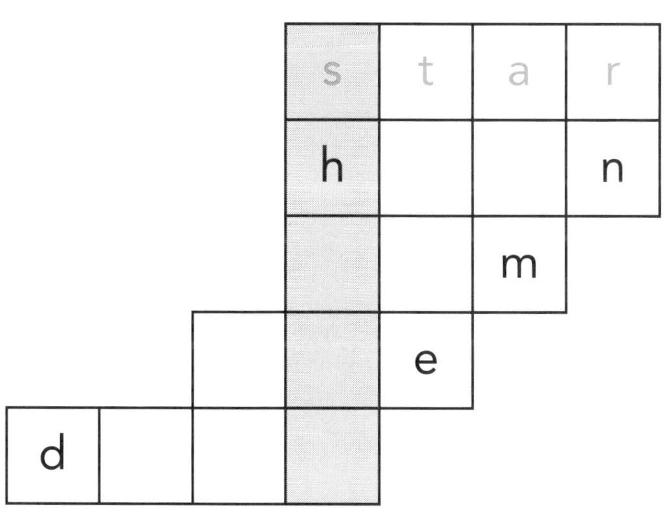

Circle the words that were not used in the puzzle.

Directions: Tell students that one spelling word fits in each line across. If completed correctly, the word reading down in the shaded boxes will match the picture. Students circle spelling words not used in the puzzle.

Monitor Comprehension

If you don't understand something, you can use a fix-up strategy.
You can **reread, read on,** or **ask for help**.

Read.

We take the bus downtown. We go to the art museum. Then we shop in the stores. It is funny when all the cars and people look very small.

What are you confused about?

I don't understand why the cars

look small.

Read on.

We look down from the top of a tall building.

What do you understand now?

They were looking down

from up high.

Read.

Ella is sad.
Then the florist brings her flowers.

The baker brings Ella a cherry pie.

What are you confused about?

I don't understand why people

____.

Read on.

Ella's friends are sorry she broke her leg.

What do you understand now?

Now I understand. ______________________________

____

Directions: Help students read the story and practice the strategy.

Use Multiple Strategies

Remember that you can use vocabulary strategies to help you figure out the meaning of words.

Synonyms are words that mean almost the same thing.

happy ⟷ glad

large ⟷ big

sad ⟷ unhappy

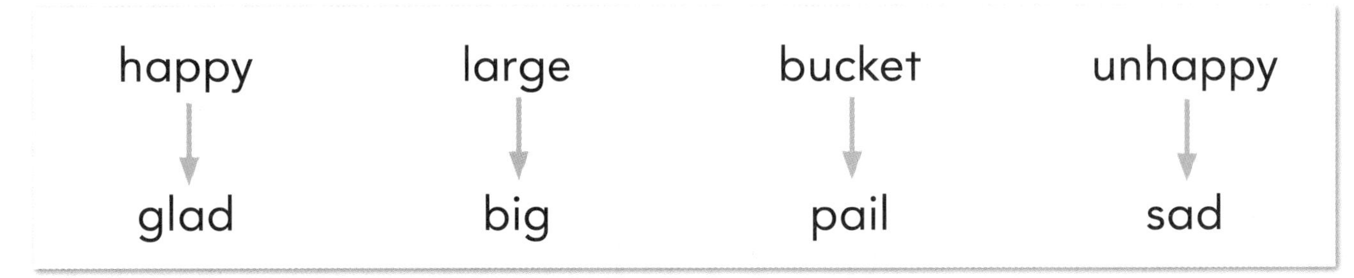

Read the sentence. Write the synonym.

We use a <u>bucket</u> to wash the car.

We use a pail to wash the car.

Read the sentences. Write the synonym.

1. 

I see the bird build a nest.

I see the bird ______________ a nest.

Read and circle the picture clues. Answer the question.

2. A blizzard covered the field with snow.

From the picture clues, I can tell that a blizzard is

a snow storm

or

a type of animal

Use a dictionary to find the meanings of any words you still need help with.

Directions: Students write a synonym for the underlined word. Then they use picture clues to find the meaning of the underlined word. Help students use the dictionary.

Recall and Retell

Recall
the story.

and

Retell
the story in your own words.

Recall a story you know.

Beginning

Little Red Riding Hood was going to her grandmother's house.

Middle

End

Retell the story.

Directions: Explain to students that when they retell a story, they tell it in their own words. Have students recall a story they know well and fill in the Story Map. For example, they may recall *Goldilocks and the Three Bears* or *Little Red Riding Hood.* Then have students retell the story to a partner orally.

Adding *-s* and *-es* to Verbs

Add *-s* or *-es* to verbs when the subject is *he, she,* or *it.*

Subject	For most verbs, add *-s.*	For verbs that end in *x, ch, sh, s,* or *z,* add *-es.*
He	He runs.	He watches a movie.
She	She walks home.	She brushes the dog.
It	It cleans the room.	It buzzes.

Write the verb.

1. He throws the ball. (throw)

2. She ______________ the ball. (catch)

3. Andy ______________ over the rope. (jump)

4. Sara ______________ her dog. (brush)

Directions: Remind students verbs show the action in a sentence. Review the rules of adding *-s* or *-es* to verbs. Then have students write the correct verb for each sentence.

Investigation Sheet

1. My Books

2. What I Learned

Directions: Read each numbered item to students. Students write the book titles that they used to collect information for the Inquiry Question. Then they draw and write what they learned from the books.

Taking Tests

Here is a question about
Where Are You, Boots?

What happened on pages 3–5?
Retell what happened.

What is the question asking you to do?
Tell what happened on pages 3–5.
How can you do this?
Remember what happened and
tell it in your own words.

First
Vanessa looked for her dog Boots.
Then
Vanessa called Boots. Boots did not come.
Last
Vanessa looked in the yard.
Boots was not there.

Look at the question on the next page.

Directions: Have students work in pairs to answer the question and retell what happened. Then have them write their answers with the group.

Taking Tests

Here is another question
about *Where Are You, Boots?*:

What happened on pages 30–32?
Recall what happened.

First

Then

Last

Use your ideas to retell what happened.

My Weekly Planner

Week of

Theme Vocabulary	
Differentiated Vocabulary	
Comprehension Strategy and Skill	Strategy: Skill:
Vocabulary Strategy	
Spelling Skill	
Fluency	Selection:
Writing and Language Arts	Writing form:
Grammar	Grammar skill:

Poem

Read this poem aloud.

The Earth Is Ours

by Alex Lydon

The Earth has soil.
It helps plants grow.
The Earth has oil.
It makes cars go.

The Earth has water.
It lets us drink.
The Earth has air.
It helps us breathe.

The earth has many things
That help us live.
The Earth is ours to share.
The Earth has much to give.

How well did you read? Circle your answer.

Directions: Follow the Teacher's Lesson Guide directions each day of the week. At the end of the week, students circle the face showing how well they read.

Draw It

Draw a picture that shows a *natural resource.*

What can you do to *conserve* this natural resource?

Directions: Students draw a picture of a natural resource, such as water, air, plants, animals, or soil. Then they write a sentence telling what they can do to conserve the natural resource.

Examples

Draw lines to connect words on the left to examples on the right.

natural resources

conserve

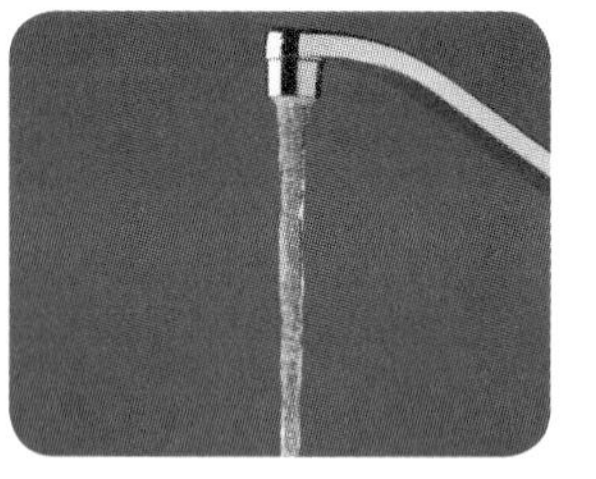

Water

Recycle

Soil

Clean up

Directions: Look at the pictures and labels. Students identify which words on the right describe natural resources and which words describe conserving. They draw lines to connect the words on the left to the examples on the right.

Words Spelled with *er, ir,* and *ur*

her	fern	bird	dirt	girl
third	turn	curl	surf	sister

Unscramble the spelling words.

1. e r h her
2. d t h r i ______
3. u n r t ______
4. t s s i r e ______
5. n r e f ______
6. t d i r ______
7. l g r i ______
8. u f r s ______
9. d b r i ______
10. u r c l ______

Directions: Review the spelling words. Then have students unscramble each jumbled word and write it on the line.

Make Connections

When you read, the story may remind you of something. This is how you **make connections**.

You can connect the story with

what you know

another book

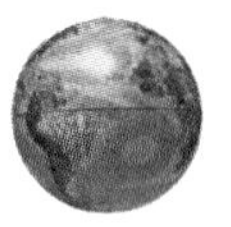
ideas in the world

Read. Look at the connection.

You can grow plants at home. Plants need water. Plants need light. Plants need space to grow.

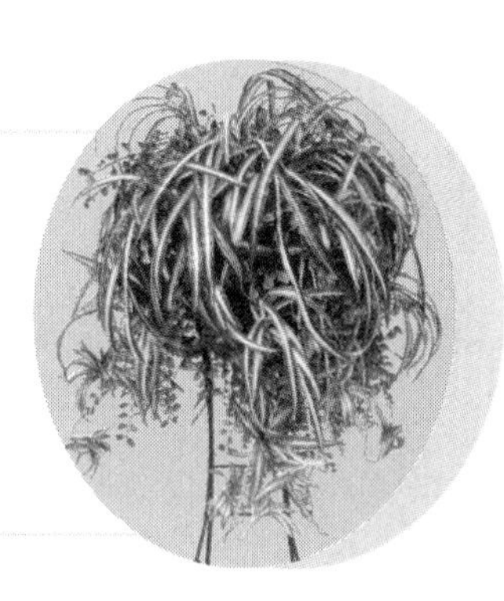

Text	Plants need space to grow. I read a book about growing pumpkins.
Self	Plants need water. I help water plants at home.
World	Plants need light. We put plants near windows to get sunshine.

Read.

It is important to care for Earth. Trash and pollution can make the water and soil dirty. Put trash in a garbage can. That helps keep Earth clean.

Write your connections.

Text	
Self	
World	

Directions: Read the text on page 168 and point out the connection. Then read the text on page 169. Help students make connections by filling in the graphic organizer.

Homophones

Homophones are words that

sound the same	have different meanings	have different spellings

hear

here

I

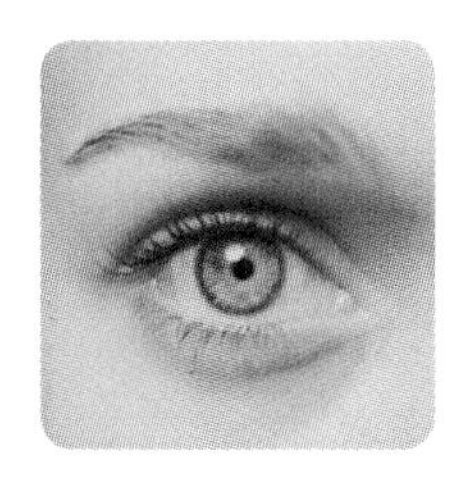

eye

Circle the correct homophone.

1. I live here / hear, next to the river.

2. I / eye walked to the store with my parents.

Circle the correct homophone.

1. My aunt lives near the **sea / see**.

2. Do you **here / hear** the music?

3. We will go **to / two** the store.

4. It is **four / for** days until my birthday!

5. Is Wendy coming **to / too**?

6. Do you **sea / see** the moon?

7. Jose has **two / too** cats.

8. Can you wink your **eye / I**?

Directions: Discuss with students the pictures and homophones on page 170. Read the sentences on page 171. Help students select the correct homophone in each sentence.

Identify Cause and Effect

Cause		Effect
A **cause** is why something happens.		An **effect** is what happens.

Write the cause and effect.

1. It was raining. We put on our raincoats.

Cause		Effect
It was raining.		

2. The boy was tired. He took a nap.

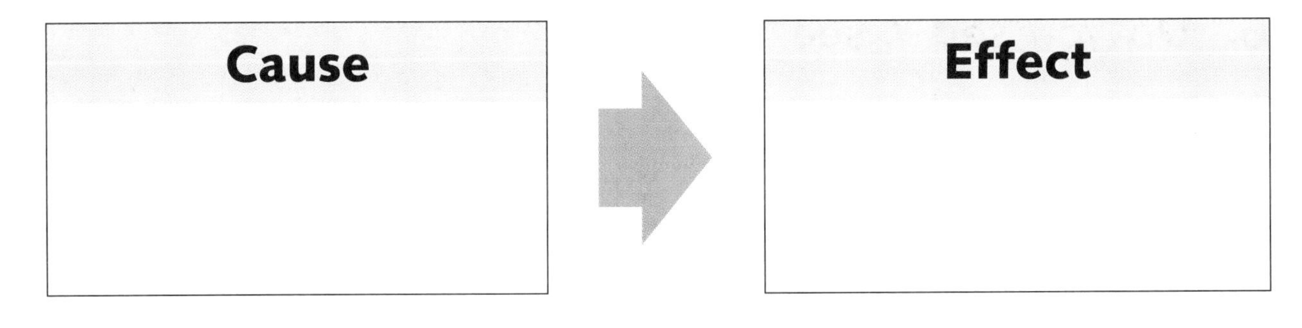

Cause		Effect

Directions: Read the questions with students. Then they work with a partner to complete the page.

Verbs for Past and Present

Verbs tell when an action happens.

Present		Past
today		yesterday
now		last week
splash	→	splashed
play	→	played

splash	splashed	play	played

Write verbs to tell about today.

Today I ____________ in the pool. I ____________ my brother.

Write verbs to tell about yesterday.

Yesterday we ____________ in the rain.

We ____________ in the puddles.

Directions: Have students fill in the blanks with verbs from the word bank.

Book of Illustrations

What is a book of illustrations?

- It is a book of pictures.
- Pictures can be photographs or drawings.
- Sometimes words tell about the pictures.
- The title is on the cover of the book.

Directions: Read the heading and each bulleted sentence to students. Have students study the example of the book of illustrations. Students use this information to help them create a book of illustrations to share their Inquiry findings.

My Weekly Planner

Week of ______________________

Theme Vocabulary

Differentiated Vocabulary

Comprehension Strategy and Skill

Strategy: ______________________

Skill: ______________________

Vocabulary Strategy

Spelling Skill

Fluency

Selection:

Writing and Language Arts

Writing form:

Grammar

Grammar skill:

Riddle

Read this riddle aloud.

A Riddle Runs Down

by Mason Goodman

We need to drink this.
What is it?

A family can go swimming
here. What is it?

This is something you need
to wash up. What is it?

Every living thing needs this. What is it?

Ready to guess? No? Then read the
letters in purple.

How well did you read? Circle your answer.

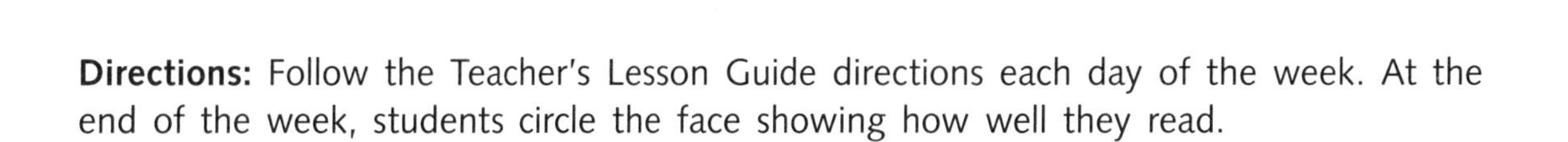

Directions: Follow the Teacher's Lesson Guide directions each day of the week. At the end of the week, students circle the face showing how well they read.

Examples

Circle places that have a lot of *space*.

open field

small closet

crowded store

large park

Draw something that causes *harm* to Earth.

Directions: Read the labels below the pictures at the top and have students circle the pictures that show places with a lot of space. Then students draw a picture at the bottom to show something that harms the environment.

Idea Completions

Circle the pictures that show a lot of space.

1. 

2. 

Write the missing word.

3. To ______________ the earth means to hurt it.
   help   harm

4. I need ______________ to run.
   space   walls

Directions: Have students look at the photos and circle the two that illustrate the word *space*. Have students read the sentences and write the correct missing words.

Words with Double Consonants

cuff	sniff	tell	still	funny
kiss	dress	jazz	fizz	will

Fill in the missing letters.

1. c u f f
2. s t i ___ ___
3. j a ___ ___
4. f u ___ ___ y
5. d r e ___ ___
6. t e ___ ___
7. s n i ___ ___
8. k i ___ ___
9. w i ___ ___
10. f i ___ ___

Write two words that rhyme.

___ ___

Directions: Review the spelling words. Have students write the double final consonants to complete each word and then the rhyming words *still* and *will*.

Make Connections

When you read, the story may remind you of something. This is called **making connections**.

Look at these connections to *Our Natural World*.

Text	Reminds Me of	Connects to
We use water for many things.	I use water to wash my hands.	○ Text ● Self ○ World
Seeds are planted in soil.	I read a book about planting a garden.	● Text ○ Self ○ World
If air has pollution, people and animals can get sick.	I saw a show about pollution.	○ Text ○ Self ● World

Read the paragraph.

Otter wanted to play. He went to the lake. Splash! He swam under the water. There was Turtle! The friends came up for air. Then they played together.

Make connections to the text. Write.

Text	Reminds Me of	Connects to
		○ Text ○ Self ○ World
		○ Text ○ Self ○ World
		○ Text ○ Self ○ World

Directions: Review the connections made to the Concepts Big Book *Our Natural World* on page 180. Then read the story on page 181 together. Students work with a partner to make connections by filling in the graphic organizer.

Use Antonyms

Antonyms are words with opposite meanings.

over ↔	under
in ↔	out
long ↔	short
near ↔	far
happy ↔	sad

Label the pictures.

over

under

Label the pictures.

clean	young	healthy	sick
huge	dirty	tiny	old

1.

clean

2. 

3. 

4. 

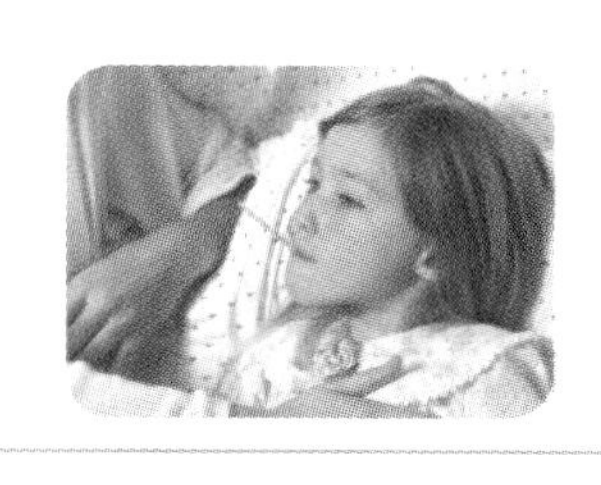

Directions: Discuss the antonyms and labels for the pictures on page 182. Have students use words from the word bank to label the pictures on page 183.

Identify Cause and Effect

A **cause** is why something happens.

An **effect** is what happens.

Cause		Effect
We heard thunder.		We went inside.

Identify the cause and the effect.

1. Carla drank water because she was thirsty.

Cause		Effect

2. We had some bananas, so we made banana bread.

Cause		Effect

Directions: Read the sentences and have students complete the page.

Adding *-ed* to Verbs

To tell about something that took place in the past, you can add *-ed* to many verbs.

Today we play in the park.

Yesterday we played at my friend's house.

Write the correct verb and add *-ed*.

clean	paint	splash	wash

1. Jill and I splashed in the puddles this morning.
2. My brother ________ the dishes.
3. Last Saturday, Dad ________ my bedroom blue.
4. Mom and I ________ the living room yesterday.

Directions: Have students choose the best verb from the word box to complete each sentence, add *-ed*, and write the verb. Read the sentences with children.

Investigation Sheet

1. My Books

2. What I Learned

Directions: Read each numbered item to students. Students write the book titles that they used to collect information for the Inquiry Question. Then they draw and write what they learned from the books.

Taking Tests

Here is a question about *Our Natural World:*

What will happen if we conserve our natural resources? (Page 19)

Ⓐ We will make them dirty.
Ⓑ We will use them all up.
Ⓒ We will cause pollution.
Ⓓ We will have enough of them.

What is the question asking for? What will happen if we take care of our natural resources?

- Will we make them dirty? No, we won't.
- Will we use them all up? No, we won't.
- Will we cause pollution? No, we won't.
- Will we have enough of them? Yes, we will. D is the correct answer.

Look at the questions on the next page.

The first question is answered for you.

Directions: With the Concepts Big Book open, work through both pages of Taking Tests with students. Remind them to pay attention to the directions, especially key words that tell how to answer the question.

Taking Tests

1. Why is air important? (Page 16)

(A) Plants, animals, and people need it to live.
(B) It has salt in it.
(C) It keeps Earth clean.
(D) Kites fly through it.

2. What does air pollution cause? (Page 18)

(A) The wind blows.
(B) Rain falls to the ground.
(C) People can get sick.
(D) People have food to eat.

3. Why do we need to conserve freshwater? (Page 20)

(A) Freshwater is found in lakes.
(B) Freshwater has a lot of salt.
(C) Rivers have freshwater.
(D) There isn't a lot of freshwater on Earth.

4. Reread page 24. What does it mean to depend on one another? (Page 24)

(A) It means to be alone.
(B) It means to harm each other.
(C) It means to need each other.
(D) It means to need a lot of space.

My Weekly Planner

Week of ______________________

Theme Vocabulary	
Differentiated Vocabulary	
Comprehension Strategy and Skill	Strategy: ______________ Skill: ______________
Vocabulary Strategy	
Spelling Skill	
Fluency	Selection:
Writing and Language Arts	Writing form:
Grammar	Grammar skill:

Lyric

Read this lyric aloud.

Earth Is Our Only Home

by Riley Ellis

Earth is our only home.
We need a place to roam.
We need the other
creatures, too.
It's our only home.

Earth is our only home.
We need a place to roam.
We need water fresh and clean.
It's our only home.

How well did you read? Circle your answer.

Directions: Follow the Teacher's Lesson Guide directions each day of the week. At the end of the week, students circle the face showing how well they read.

Draw It

Draw.

1. A thing that I **cherish** is ______________________.

2. A person I **cherish** is ______________________.

Directions: Discuss the things students cherish, such as a favorite object, and the people they cherish, such as family and friends. Then have students complete the sentences in their own words and draw a picture for their answers.

Related Words

listen	care for	conserve

Use the words to write sentences.

1.  I **cherish** my friends.

I listen when they are sad.

2.  I **cherish** my family.

3. 

I **cherish** Earth.

Directions: Read and discuss the related words in the box. Explain the example to students. *Because I cherish my friends, I listen when they are sad. How do you show that you **cherish** your friends?* Students write what they do to show that they cherish their families and Earth.

Words Spelled with *a, a_e*

sale	grape	chase	make	their
came	late	able	acorn	favorite

Fill in the crossword puzzle.

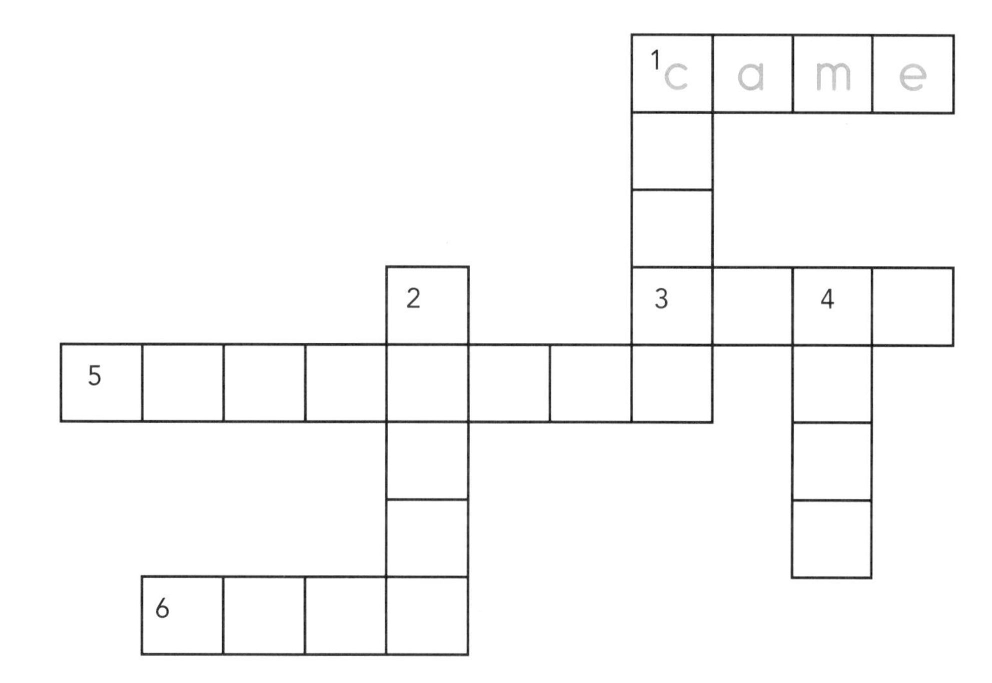

Across

1. got here
3. when things cost less
5. the thing you like best
6. to create

Down

1. to run after
2. a fruit
4. not on time

Circle the words that are left in the word bank.

Directions: Review the spelling words. Have students use the words to fill in the crossword puzzle.

Visualize

When you **visualize**, you make pictures in your mind.

Read this sentence. What do you see?

The tall glass of lemonade was ice cold.

I see a glass of lemonade with ice in it.

Use the Strategy

1. **Read** the text.
2. **Think** about the describing words.
3. **Make pictures** in your mind.
4. **Tell** about the pictures you visualize.

Visualize. Then draw and describe.

1. The old, green tractor plowed the rich, black soil.

2. The bright, colorful bird sat high up on a tree branch.

Directions: Read and discuss page 194. Read the sentences aloud on page 195. Students draw and describe what they visualize.

Picture Clues

Picture clues can help tell the meaning of a word you do not know.

Read. Look at the underlined word.

On our trip, we saw beautiful mountains and the valley below.

Write the picture clues you see. Write the meaning of the word.

Word I Don't Know	Picture Clues	Meaning of Word
valley	mountains There is a low place between the mountains.	A valley must be the low land between mountains.

Read. Look at the underlined word.

1. Whales like to leap out of the sea.

Write the picture clues you see. Write the meaning of the word.

Word I Don't Know	Picture Clues	Meaning of Word
leap		

Read. Look at the underlined word.

2. Two birds suddenly soar into the sky.

Write the picture clues you see. Write the meaning of the word.

Word I Don't Know	Picture Clues	Meaning of Word
soar		

Directions: Students use picture clues and fill in the charts to figure out the meanings of the underlined words.

Setting

Read the story. Answer the questions.

Sally woke up early on Saturday. She went with Mom to a yard sale. She saw old books, toys, and dishes for sale. Then she saw an old doll wearing a red dress. Its eyes opened and closed. Sally loved the doll. Now the doll lives with Sally.

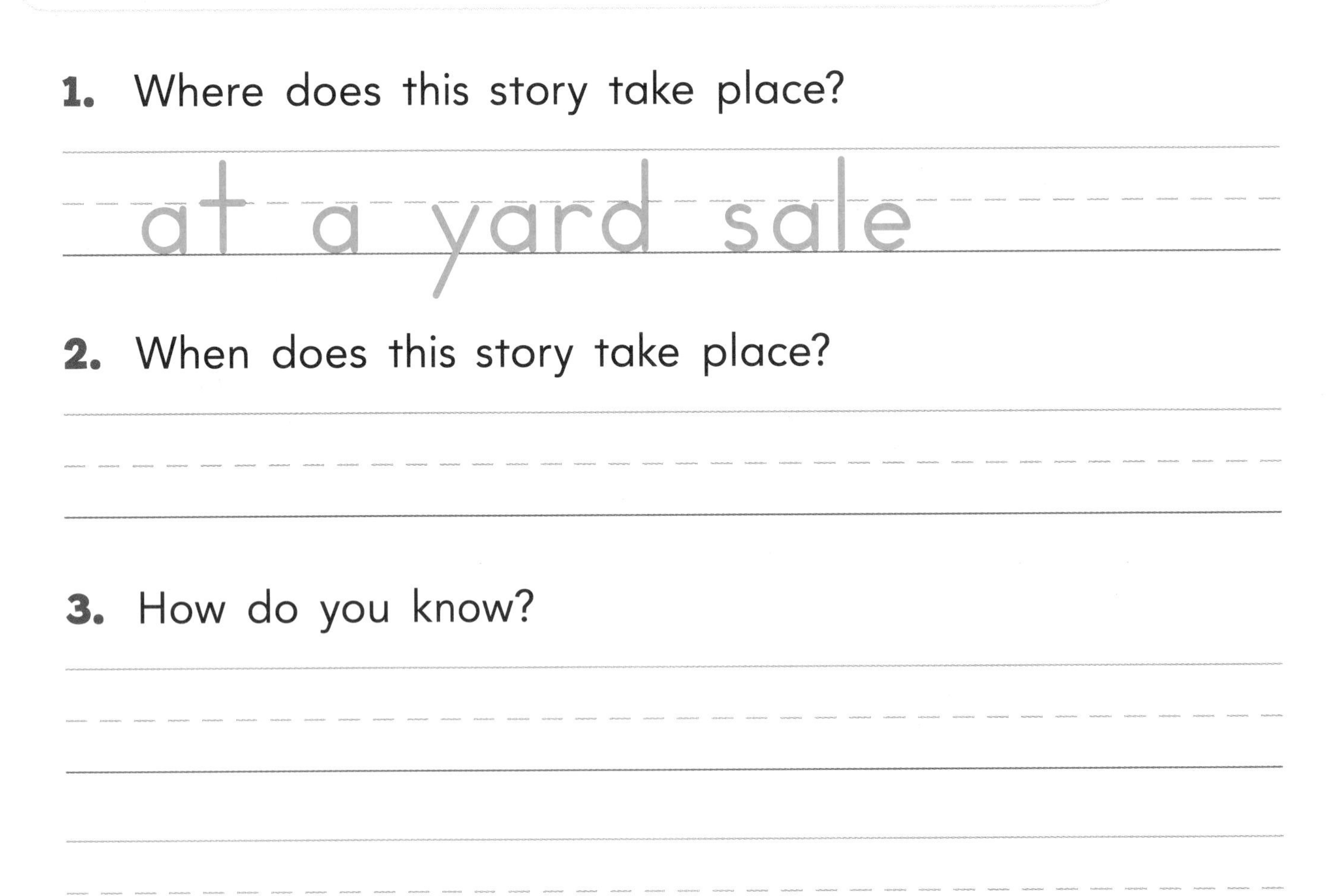

1. Where does this story take place?

at a yard sale

2. When does this story take place?

3. How do you know?

Directions: Help students read the story and answer the questions.

Read and Respond

Think about what you read in *This Is Our Earth*. Then answer the questions.

1. What did you like best about the story?

2. What stories have you read that are like this one?

3. Which place in the story is most like the place where you live? Why?

Directions: Have students think about what they read in *This Is Our Earth*. Then have them answer the questions.

Draw Conclusions

To **draw conclusions**, fill in pieces of information.

Use information from the text and what you know.

Read.

The park ranger wore a brown uniform. She talked to the children about the animals. Then she told them about the park rules.

Circle the best conclusion.

What does a park ranger do?

A park ranger helps people find the park.

A park ranger gives people information about the park.

A park ranger drives people around the park.

Directions: Help students read the text. Then have them circle the best conclusion.

Using the Verbs *is/are*

Use *is* or *are* to tell about other people, places, or things.

Use *is* for one person, place, or thing.

Bob *is* my friend.

Use *are* for more than one person, place, or thing.

Pam and Sue *are* my friends.

Write *is* or *are*.

1. 

These two ladies 

bankers.

2. 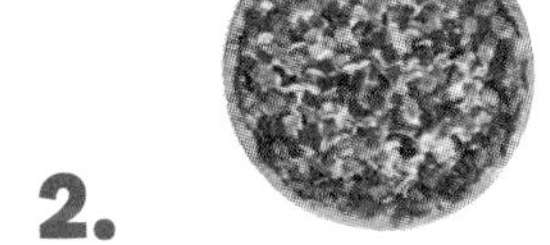

We ________ eating pizza!

3. 

My town ________ pretty.

Directions: Explain that *is* and *are* are used to name or describe things, not to show action. Read the sentences aloud. Have students write the correct verb to complete each sentence.

Collage

What is a collage?

- A collage can be made of many different kinds of pictures.
- Collages tell about a topic or tell a story.
- Photographs can be cut out of newspapers or magazines.
- Pictures can be made out of paper or drawn.
- Labels are sometimes used to tell about the pictures.

Directions: Read the headings and each bulleted sentence to students. Have students study the example of the collage. Students use this information to help them create a collage to share their Inquiry findings.

My Weekly Planner

Week of ______________________

Theme Vocabulary	
Differentiated Vocabulary	
Comprehension Strategy and Skill	Strategy: Skill:
Vocabulary Strategy	
Spelling Skill	
Fluency	Selection:
Writing and Language Arts	Writing form:
Grammar	Grammar skill:

Play

Read this play aloud.

One Can

by Kim Ross

Doug: Stop! Don't throw that can in the trash!

Sammy: What are you talking about?

Ana: That can goes in recycling.

Sammy: Come on. It's just one can!

Ana: They add up.

Doug: Just imagine if everyone at this school recycled one can.

Ana: That would save hundreds of cans.

Sammy: I never thought of it like that!

How well did you read? Circle your answer.

Directions: Follow the Teacher's Lesson Guide directions each day of the week. At the end of the week, students circle the face showing how well they read.

Examples

Circle the correct word.

1. **natural resource** **harm** **conserve**

turn off water

recycle

2. **space** **cherish** **conserve**

large room

open field

3. **conserve** **natural resource** **space**

water

soil

4. **cherish** **harm** **natural resource**

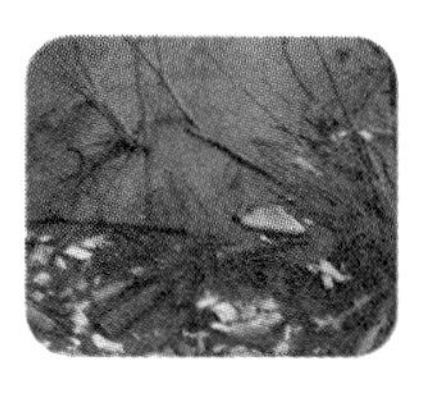

trash

pollution

Directions: Students look carefully at each photo. Help them read the labels. Then students circle the best word to describe the pictures.

Sentence Completion

Complete the sentences.

1. **Natural resources** that I see every day are air ________ and ________.

2. One way to **conserve** water is to ________________________.

3. One thing that can **harm** plants and animals is ________________.

4. A place near our school that has open **space** is ________________.

5. To **cherish** something means to ________________________.

Directions: Help students complete the sentences with examples that tell about the vocabulary words.

Words Spelled with *i, i_e*

like	side	bite	nice	I'm
five	nine	kind	child	sometimes

Write the missing letters.

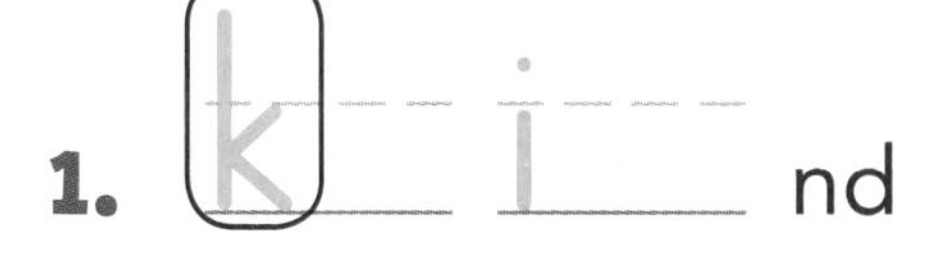

1. k i ___ nd
2. ___ ___ k ___
3. ___ it ___
4. s ___ ___ ___

5. ___ ___ v ___
6. ___ ___ ___ ld
7. ___ ___ c ___
8. I' ___

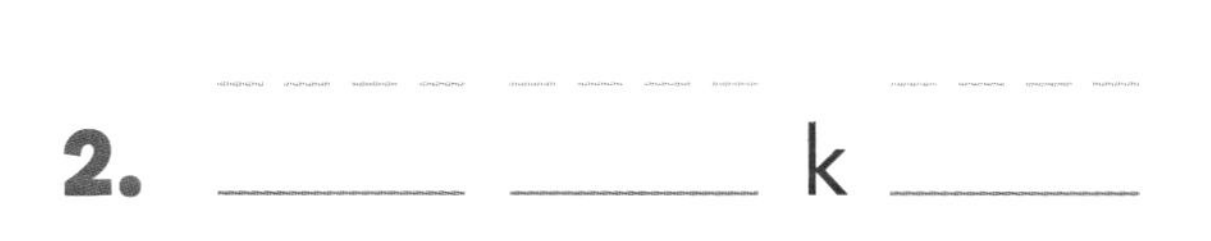

Write the letters in the circles. Use the letters to write a word.

___ ___ ___ ___ ___________

Circle the words that are left.

Directions: Review the spelling words. Students write the letters that fit in the missing blanks for each word. Then students write the letters from the circles and unscramble them to write the word *bike*. Students circle the remaining spelling words.

Visualize

When you **visualize**, you make pictures in your mind.

Use the Strategy

1. **Read** the text.

2. **Think** about the describing words.

3. **Make pictures** in your mind.

4. **Tell** about the pictures you visualize.

Visualize. Then draw and describe.

The storm covered everything outdoors with ice. The heavy ice broke branches off trees. It knocked down telephone poles. People fell on the slippery sidewalks.

Directions: Read aloud page 208 and connect the four points to the illustrations. Then read the sentences on page 209. Students draw and describe what they visualize.

Use Multiple Strategies

Remember that you can use vocabulary strategies to help you figure out the meaning of words.

Vocabulary strategies

Homophones are words that sound alike but have different spellings and meanings.

An antonym is a word that means the opposite of another word.

Picture clues can help you understand the meaning of a word.

Write the correct homophone.

1. **for** **four**

Do you really have ________ brothers?

Sally had cereal ________ breakfast.

Read. Look at the underlined word.

2. Our soccer team won a <u>trophy</u>.

Write the picture clues you see. Write the meaning of the word.

Word I Don't Know	Picture Clues	Meaning of Word
trophy		

Write an antonym for the underlined word.

3. The giraffe is very <u>tall</u>. ________

Directions: Help students read sentences. Students choose the correct homophone to write in each blank. Students use picture clues to determine the meaning of *trophy*. Then students write an antonym for *tall*.

Draw Conclusions

When you **draw conclusions**, you fill in information that the author doesn't tell you.

Read.

Ari and Isa were at the beach.
"Pick up your bottle," Ari said.
"Why?" said Isa.
"Lots of animals live here. Plastic bottles can harm the animals," Ari told her.

Fill in the chart.

What will Isa do?

Isa left a plastic bottle.

Isa will

Directions: Help students read the text. Then they draw a conclusion and fill in the graphic organizer.

Using the Verbs *was/were*

To tell about the past, use *was* or *were.*

I He/She It	**was**	at school yesterday.
You	**were**	
We They	**were**	

Write *was* or *were.*

1.  Ronald was sick yesterday.

2.  They ________ at the museum.

3.  Kim ________ tired last night.

4.  We ________ at the beach.

Directions: Review *was* and *were.* Have students write the correct verb to complete each sentence.

Investigation Sheet

1. My Books

2. What I Learned

Directions: Read each numbered item to students. Students write the book titles that they used to collect information for the Inquiry Question. Then they draw and write what they learned from the books.

Taking Tests

Here is a question about *This Is Our Earth.*

Read page 6. What do you picture in your mind when you read this page? Which words in the selection help you visualize?

What is the question asking you to do? Tell what you picture in your mind when you read.

How can you answer this question? Look for describing words that help you visualize.

Words from Text	What Do You Picture in Your Mind?
• mountains so high	• I picture big, tall mountains that touch the sky.
• valleys below	• I picture low places between and around the mountains.
• green, grassy plain	• I picture a flat green place where animals can eat the grass.

Directions: With the literature book open, work through both pages of Taking Tests with students. Remind them to pay attention to the directions, especially key words that tell how to answer the question.

Taking Tests

Here is another question about *This Is Our Earth:*

Read page 16. Write words from the selection that help you visualize. What do you picture in your mind when you read the words?

Words from Text	What I Picture in My Mind
•	•
•	•
•	•

Write what you picture when you read page 16.

Rules for Group Work

1. Listen quietly while others are talking.

2. Work with your group.

3. Share and take turns.

4. Focus on your task.

5. Ask a partner questions.

Directions: Read the Rules for Group Work to students. Tell students that they will need to follow these rules when working in their Inquiry Groups.

Acknowledgments

Art Credits:

©The McGraw-Hill Companies, Inc., would like to thank the following illustrators for their contributions: Jayoung Cho, Antonio Vincenti, Vendula Hegerova, Pascale Constantin, Linda Bronson, John Ott, Gideon Kendall, Alexi Natchev, Margie Moore, Mick Reid, Deborah Zemke, Deborag Borgo, Daniel Griffon, Drew Rose, Diane Paterson.

Photo Credits:

Cover (tl) ©Dynamic Graphics Group/Punch Stock, (tr) ©Dorling Kindersley/Getty Images, (bl) Jeremy Woodhouse/Getty Images, (br) Ariel Skelley/Blend Images/Getty Images; **2** ©Steve Gorton/Dorling Kindersley/Getty Images; **3** (tl) ©Photodisc Collection/GettyImages, (tr) ©Eclipse Studios, (c) ©Gaetano Images Inc./Alamy, (b) ©Tim Pannell/Corbis; **4** (t-b) ©Photodisc/GettyImages, ©Royalty-Free/CORBIS, ©Comstock Images/Alamy, ©Stockbyte/PunchStock, ©Stockbyte/PunchStock; **5** (tl) ©Authors Image/PunchStock, (tr) ©Siede Preis/Getty Images, (bl) ©The McGraw-Hill Companies, Inc/Ken Karp photographer, (br) ©Barbara Penoyar/Getty Images; **6** (l) ©Royalty-Free/CORBIS, (c) ©Digital Vision Ltd, (r) ©Stockdisc/GettyImages; **7** (t) ©Ariel Skelley/Blend Images/GettyImages, (b) ©BrandXPictures/PunchStock; **8** (t) ©i love images/Alamy, (b) ©Royalty-Free/CORBIS; **9** (t-b) ©UpperCut Images/Alamy, ©The McGraw-Hill Companies Inc./Ken Cavanagh Photographer, ©Brand X Pictures/PunchStock, ©Punchstock/BananaStock; **10** (tl) ©Image Club, (tr) ©McGraw-Hill Companies, Inc./Gary He, photographer, (bl) ©1996 PhotoDisc, Inc./GettyImages, (br) ©Ingram Publishing/Alamy; **11** (t-b) ©Ed-Imaging, ©Andersen Ross/GettyImages, BrandXPictures, ©Goodshoot/PunchStock; **12** (t-b) ©David Buffington/Getty Images, ©Scott T. Baxter/Getty Images, ©Scott T. Baxter/Getty Images, Laurence Mouton/Photoalto/PictureQuest, ©Ingram Publishing/Alamy; **16** (t) ©Getty Images/Blend Images, (c) ©Nicola Sutton/LifeFile/Getty Images, (b) ©Buccina Studios/Getty Images; **18** (l) ©Jay Freis/Digital Vision/Alamy Images, (r) ©Jack Hollingsworth/Getty Images; **19** (tl) ©BananaStock/SuperStock, (tr) ©Image100, (b) ©Mark Andersen/Getty Images; **20** ©Jack Hollingsworth/Corbis; **22** (t) ©Image Club, (c) ©Photodisc/GettyImages, (b) ©Chris Robbins/Getty Images; **23** ©Rayes/Digital Vision/Getty Images; **28** ©2008 Jupiterimages Corporation; **29** ©IngramPublishing/SuperStock; **30** (l-r) ©Stockbyte/PunchStock, ©Image Source/Punchstock, ©Ed-Imaging, ©BananaStock/age footstock; **33** ©Stockdisc/PunchStock; **34** (l) ©Siri Stafford/GettyImages, (r) ©SuperStock Inc.; **36** (t-b) ©Lothar/GettyImages, ©The McGraw-Hill Companies; **38** (l) ©Dynamic Graphics/Creatas/PictureQuest, (c) ©Corbis/PunchStock, (r) ©White Rock/Getty Images; **39** (t) ©Comstock Images, (c) ©ImageDJ/Alamy, (r) ©Corbis/PunchStock; **42** ©Reflexstock/Pureline/mauritius images; **48** ©imagebroker/Alamy; **49** (t) ©Digital Vision/Getty Images, (c) ©IT Stock/PunchStock, (b) ©Getty Images; **50** ©Image Club; **56** ©Digital Vision; **57** (tl) ©Royalty-Free/CORBIS, (tc) ©Redmond Durrell/Alamy, (tr) ©Eureka/Alamy, (cl) ©C Squared Studios/Getty Images, (c) ©The McGraw-Hill Companies, Inc./Michael Scott photographer, (cr) ©Ingram Publishing/Alamy, (bl) ©Getty Images, (bl) ©Ian Coles, (bc) ©Comstock Images/Alamy, (br) ©Getty Images; **58** (tl) ©BananaStock/PunchStock, (bl) ©Comstock/JupiterImages, (rt-b) ©Digital Vision/Getty Images, ©Ian Coles, ©Royalty-Free/CORBIS, ©Comstock Images, ©Stockbyte, ©The McGraw-Hill Companies, Inc./Michael Scott photographer; **60** (l) ©Royalty-Free/CORBIS, (r) ©Kris Legg/Alamy; **61** (t) ©Ingram Publishing/Alamy, (b) ©Tim Hall/Digital Vision/Getty Images; **65** (t-b) ©Geostock/Getty Images, ©C Squared Studios/Getty Images, ©Comstock Images/Alamy, ©Comstock/PictureQuest; **66** (tl) ©Corbis/PictureQuest, (tr) ©Digital Vision/Veer, (bl) ©Randy Faris/Corbis, (br) ©Royalty-Free/CORBIS; **69** (tl-b) ©Natphotos/Digital Vision/Getty Images, ©Ryan McVay/Getty Images , ©Royalty-Free/CORBIS, ©Royalty-Free/CORBIS, (tc-b) ©The McGraw-Hill Companies, Inc/Ken Karp photographer, ©Burke/Triolo Productions/Getty Images, ©The McGraw-Hill Companies, ©Royalty-Free/CORBIS, (tr-b) ©Gary Kramer, USDA Natural Resources Conservation Service, ©SW Productions/GettyImages, ©Royalty-Free/CORBIS, ©Geostock/Getty Images; **70** (t-b) ©Comstock/PunchStock, ©Creatas/PictureQuest, Martin Harvey/Digital Vision/GettyImages; **71** (tl-bl) ©Royalty Free/Corbis, ©Burke Triolo Productions/GettyImages, ©Getty Images, ©Royalty-Free/CORBIS, ©Thinkstock/Jupiterimages, ©Getty Images, (tr) ©Royalty-Free/CORBIS; **73** ©Royalty-Free/CORBIS; **74** ©Getty Images; **75** ©PhotoAlto/PictureQuest; **76** (tl) ©Digital Vision/Getty Images, (tr) ©hotoAlto/PictureQuest, (bl) ©Royalty-Free/CORBIS, (br) ©Getty Images; **77** ©The McGraw-Hill Companies Inc./Ken Cavanagh Photographer; **82** ©McGraw Hill Companies; **83** (t-b) ©Charles Smith/Corbis, ©ImageDJ/Alamy, ©Noel Hendrickson/GettyImages, ©Photodisc Collection/GettyImages; **86** (l) ©Pepiera Tom/Iconotec.com, (r) ©Creatas/PunchStock; **87** ©S. Meltzer/PhotoLink/Getty Images; **88** (t-b) ©Ingram Publishing/SuperStock, ©Digital Archive Japan/Alamy, ©Stockdisc/PunchStock, ©BrandXPictures/PunchStock, ©Studio Photogram/Alamy; **89** (l) ©Photodisc, (r) ©Studio Photogram/Alamy; **92** ©Royalty Free; **93** (tl) ©Dynamic Graphics/JupiterImages, (tc) ©MedioImages, (tr)Blend Images/SuperStock, (bl) Comstock Images/Jupiter Images, (bc) ©Image Source/Getty Images, (br) ©Ken Usami/Getty Images; **96** ©Photodisc Collection/Getty Images; **99** (t) ©Stockbyte/PunchStock, (c) ©Photodisc/Getty Images, (b) ©Burke/Triolo Productions/BrandXPictures/Getty Images; **102** ©Johann Helgason/Alamy; **103** ©Comstock/PunchStock; **103** ©The McGraw-Hill Companies Inc./Dot Box Inc. photographer; **104** (l) ©Geostock/Getty Images, (r) ©Royalty-Free/CORBIS; **111** (t) ©Getty Images/Blend Images, (c) ©BrandX Pitures/PunchStock, **115** (l) ©Getty Images/Digital Vision, (r) ©Photolink/Getty Images; **118** ©Blend Images/Alamy; **119** (t-b) ©Getty Images/Digital Vision, ©Creatas/PunchStock, ©Jack Hollingsworth/Getty Images, ©Michael Matisse/Getty Images; **120** (l) ©The McGraw-Hill Companies, Inc./Andrew Resek, (r) ©The McGraw-Hill Companies, Inc./John Flournoy; **123** (l-r, t-b) ©Getty Images, ©Image State Royalty Free/Alamy Images, ©BrandXPictures/PunchStock, ©Lars Niki, ©Getty Images/Photodisc, Royalty-Free/CORBIS, (Comstock Images/Alamy, ©The McGraw-Hill Companies Inc./Ken Cavanagh Photographer, ©The McGraw-Hill Companies Inc./Ken Cavanagh Photographer, ©Ingram Publishing/Alamy, ©Siede Preis/Getty Images, ©Ingram Publishing/Alamy, ©Photodisc/Getty Images; **126** ©Royalty-Free/CORBIS; **127** ©Creatas Images/PictureQuest; **128** (t) ©Burke/Triolo/Brand X Pictures/Jupiterimages, (b) ©Ryan McVay/Getty Images; **129** ©S. Alden/PhotoLink/Getty Images; **130** (t) ©Comstock/Jupiter Images (c) ©Banana Stock/Alamy, (b) ©NASA; **131** (lt-b) ©2009 Jupiterimages Corporation, ©Purestock/PunchStock, ©Royalty-Free/Corbis, ©Comstock Images, (rt-b) ©The McGraw-Hill Companies, Inc./Jill Braaten, photographer, ©Eyewire (Photdisc)/Getty Images, ©RubberBall Productions/Getty Images, ©Punchstock/BananaStock; **136** ©The McGraw-Hill Companies; **137** (t) ©Stockbyte/Getty Images, (c) ©Dynamic Graphics/JupiterImages, (b) ©RubberBall Productions/Getty Images; **141** (t) ©Jack Hollingsworth/Corbis, (c) ©Brand X

Pictures/PunchStock, (b) ©Royalty-Free/CORBIS; **142** ©Michael Blann/Getty Images; **143** (t) ©Image Source/Alamy, (b) ©UpperCut Images/Alamy; **144** (t) ©Stockbyte/Getty Images, (b) ©Getty Images/Digital Vision; **147** (t-b) ©Royalty-Free/Corbis, ©Digital Vision/Getty Images, ©SW Productions/GettyImages, ©Jarvell Jardey/Alamy; **148** ©Dave Pattison/Alamy; **153** ©Sam Toren/Alamy; **154** ©Photo by Gary Wilson, USDA Natural Resources Conservation Service; **155** ©Royalty-Free/CORBIS; **156** ©C Squared Studios/Getty Images; **157** (t) ©Image Source/Getty Images, (b) ©Sherburne/PhotoLink/Getty Images; **159** (t-b) ©Ken Karp for MMH, ©Lars Niki, ©Asia Images Group/Getty Images; **164** ©Fotosonline/Alamy **166** (t-b) ©Don Farrall/Getty Images, ©Ariel Skelley/GettyImages, ©Pixtal/AGE Fotostock, ©Leland Bobbe/Digital Vision/GettyImages; **168** (c) ©2009 JUPITERIMAGES, (r) ©Ingram Publishing/Alamy, (b) ©Ingram Publishing/Alamy; **169** ©Ariel Skelley/Getty Image; **170** (t-b) ©D. Berry/PhotoLink/Getty Images, ©Asia Images Group/Getty Images, ©Digital Vision/Getty Images, ©C Squared Studios/Getty Images; **172** (t) ©Tim Hall/Photodisc/Getty Images, (b) ©BananaStock/PunchStock; **173** (t) ©Royalty-Free/CORBIS, (b) ©Andersen Ross/Photodisc/Getty Images; **177** (tl) ©Brand X Pictures/PunchStock, tr) ©2009 Jupiterimages Corporation, (bl) ©Digital Vision/Getty Images, (br) ©Brand X Pictures/PunchStock; **178** (tl) ©C. Borland/PhotoLink/Getty Images, (tr) ©B2MProductions, (br) ©Kai Honkanen/PhotoAlto; **180** ©Ariel Skelley/Blend Images/Getty Images; **181** ©Alan and Sandy Carey/Getty Images; **182** (l) ©Royalty-Free/CORBIS, (r) ©Comstock Images/Alamy; **183** (lt-b) ©PhotoLink/Getty Images, ©IT Stock Free/Alamy, ©ananastock/PictureQuest, ©SuperStock Inc., (rt-b) ©Rim Light/PhotoLink/Getty Images, ©Ingram Publishing/Alamy, ©Royalty-Free/CORBI; **184** (t) ©Robert Manella for MMH, (b) ©D. Hurst/Alamy; **190** ©NASA; **192** (t) ©Laurence Mouton/Photoalto/PictureQuest, (c) ©JupiterImages, (b) ©Ariel Skelley/Getty Images; **194** (l) ©Stockbyte/PunchStock, (r) ©SW Productions/Getty Images; **196** ©Digital Vision/PunchStock; **197** (t) ©Royalty-Free/CORBIS, (b) ©Creatas/PunchStock; **198** ©David Sacks/Getty Images; **200** (t) ©Lisa Zador/Getty Images, (b) ©John Lund/Sam Diephuis/Getty Images; **201** (t) ©Royalty-Free/CORBIS, (c) ©Brand X Pictures/Alamy, (b) ©Hisham Ibrahim/Getty Images; **202** ©The McGraw-Hill Companies Inc./Ken Cavanagh Photographer; **205** (tl-b) ©Brand X Pictures/PunchStock, ©C. Borland/PhotoLink/Getty Images, ©Ron Nichols, USDA Natural Resources Conservation Service, ©PhotoAlto, (tr-b) ©Image Club, ©Don Hammond/Age Fotostock, ©Nancy R. Cohen/Getty Images, ©David Zurick; **208** (t) ©The McGraw-Hill Companies, Inc./Jill Braaten, photographer, (c) ©Stock4BRF, (b) ©SW Productions/Brand X Pictures/Getty Images; **211** ©Alistair Berg/Getty Images; **212** ©Getty Images/PhotoAlto; **213** (t-b) ©Pixtal/age footstock, ©Getty Images/Uppercut RF, ©Stockdisc/PunchStock, ©Stockbyte/Getty Images.